All on Stage

Book 1: group scenes for young players

Selected by Mary Greenslade

Samuel French — London
New York - Toronto - Hollywood

ISBN 0 573 19011 9

CONTENTS

ACKNOWLEDGEMENTS

For permission to print or reprint copyright extracts from copyright works in this volume the compiler and publishers are grateful to the following authors, translators, their representatives and publishers. Every effort has been made to trace the copyright holders, but should any inaccurate information be given below please contact the publishers.

An Alien Stole My Skateboard © 1993 by Randall Lewton. By permission of the author. Published by Samuel French Ltd.

The Burston Drum © 1989 by Ellen Dryden (book). By permission of Casarotto Ramsay Ltd, National House, 60-66 Wardour Street, London W1V 3HP, to whom all enquiries regarding professional performance should be made. Published by Samuel French Ltd.

Dreams of Anne Frank © 1993 by Bernard Kops. By permission of the author. Published by Samuel French Ltd.

The Evil Eye of Gondôr © 1983 by Bryan Owen. By permission of the author. Published by Samuel French Ltd.

Grinling Gibbons and the Plague of London © 1977 by Brian Way. Reprinted by permission of Baker's Plays, Boston, MA 02111, USA.

Hans, the Witch and the Gobbin © 1959 by Alan Cullen. By permission of the author. Published by Samuel French Ltd.

Hard Times © 1987 by Stephen Jeffreys. By permission of Casarotto Ramsay Ltd, National House, 60-66 Wardour Street, London W1V 3HP, to whom all enquiries regarding professional performance should be made. Published by Samuel French Ltd.

Hiawatha © 1981 by Michael Bogdanov. By permission of Michael Imison Playwrights Ltd, 28 Almeida Street, London N1 1TD. Published by Samuel French Ltd.

Hijack Over Hygenia © 1974 by David Wood. By permission of the author. Published by Samuel French Ltd.

Jane Eyre by Willis Hall, © 1994 by Willis Hall Productions. By permission of Alexandra Cann Representation, 337 Fulham Road, London SW10 9TW. Published by Samuel French Ltd.

The Lion, the Witch and the Wardrobe. Original novel © 1950 by C.S. Lewis Pte Ltd. Adaptation © 1987 by C.S. Lewis Pte Ltd/Glyn Robbins. Reproduced by permission of Film Rights Ltd, 483 Southbank House, Black Prince Road, Albert Embankment, London SE1 7SJ and Curtis Brown Group Ltd, Haymarket House, 28-29 Haymarket, London SW1 4SP. Published by Samuel French Ltd.

PREFACE

With the emphasis more and more on training in oral communication skills in schools, a high standard of performance becomes increasingly important.

Teachers of Drama and English know that preparation time spent on a good script is not only satisfying but reaps its rewards on stage. The process of studying a scene in depth is made more enjoyable when the background of a scene is gradually built up in discussion by the group working as a disciplined team. This involves the vocal and physical aspects of characterization, and the relationship and reactions of characters one to another. 'The approach to every role is an act of research' (Eric Hollis, *The Performer*, the Guildhall Journal, November 1993). It also includes the understanding of style in performance, with an awareness of period, language and the rhythm of speech patterns. This, in turn, means clarity of speech, audibility and projection. Within this framework, emotional levels, timing and climaxes must be realized and communicated with conviction. Gradually, the truth of the scene is understood and appreciated. This leads to a sense of exhilaration in performance, when a polished piece of drama is produced.

Within the two volumes of *All on Stage*, there is material for classroom drama lessons, for concerts, festivals and group performance examinations at all levels. Each excerpt is self-contained, but will need thought in planning, and with imagination, originality and inventiveness, the director and the production team will 'orchestrate' the scene and bring the script to life. It is amazing what a high standard may be accomplished with careful use of space, simple imaginative staging, an eye to grouping and levels and, most important, with an energetic, enthusiastic group of players and backstage crew achieving together and responding to direction.

Although each of these scenes has an introduction to help set it in context, it is always important to study the whole play for a thorough knowledge and appreciation of character, plot and style. There is comedy and tragedy and a cross-section of modern and classical, including lively adaptations from novels, and scenes for small and large casts, some with challenging crowd scenes. May you enjoy performing in them all.

So now: 'Go make you ready ... Bid the players make haste.'

MARY GREENSLADE

CASTS AND PLAYING TIMES

NB. The playing times indicated are approximate.

An Alien Stole My Skateboard
 M6 F1 (with doubling). Extras. Playing time: 24 minutes.
The Burston Drum
 M1 F3, 4 boys 8 girls. Playing time: 17 minutes.
Dreams of Anne Frank
 M4 F4. Playing time: 15 minutes.
The Evil Eye of Gondôr
 10 main speaking parts (male or mixed). Extras. Playing time: 16 minutes.
Grinling Gibbons and the Plague of London
 M6 F2. Playing time: 12 minutes.
Hans, the Witch and the Gobbin
 M6 F3, 2 M or F. 1 female voice. Playing time: 30 minutes.
Hard Times
 M2 F2. Playing time: 16 minutes.
Hiawatha
 Flexible. Playing time: 16 minutes.
Hijack Over Hygenia
 M6 F4. Playing time: 19 minutes.
Jane Eyre
 M4 F7, 2 M or F, 1 girl. Extras. Playing time: 28 minutes.
The Lion, the Witch and the Wardrobe
 M6 F2, 2 boys 2 girls. Extras. Playing time: 14 minutes.
A Little Princess
 M2 F3, 8 girls. Playing time: 16 minutes.
The Lords of Creation
 22 characters. Extras. Playing time: 15 minutes.
The Monster That Ate 3B
 14 characters. Extras. Playing time: 11 minutes.
Oliver Twist
 13 characters. Extras. Playing time: 16 minutes.
Our Day Out
 M3 F2, 7 boys 3 girls. Extras. Playing time: 18 minutes.
The Play of the Royal Astrologers
 9 characters. Playing time: 18 minutes.

Quest for the Whooperdink
   FIRST SCENE M3 F2. Playing time: 11 minutes. SECOND SCENE M3 F2, 3M or F.
   Playing time: 13 minutes.
The Railway Children
   M2 F1, 3 boys 3 girls. Playing time: 15 minutes.
Robin Hood
   M8 F4, 1M or F. Extras. Playing time: 12 minutes.
Second from Last in the Sack Race
   M7 F3, may be played by M5 F2. Playing time: 13 minutes.
Stone Soup
   M5 F5. Extras. Playing time: 14 minutes.
Think of the Magic
   M8 F9. Extras. Playing time: 20 minutes.
The Water Babies
   M7 F4. 4 off-stage voices. Playing time: 12 minutes.

Also published by Samuel French Ltd

SCENES FOR TWO
Book I Duologues for Young Players

SCENES FOR TWO
Book II Duologues for Girls and Women

Edited by Mary Greenslade and Anne Harvey

AN ALIEN STOLE MY SKATEBOARD
by Randall Lewton

Meeting in Don's bedroom, he and his two friends, Bryn and Shaun, become involved in a fantasy game that carries them into the activities on planet Wuldor with exciting and amusing results. The play opens with an effective scene set in the royal palace on Wuldor which sets the mood and sinister atmosphere. In the following contrasting scene, Bryn and Prince Erfa are about to change places by the power of Dwimor, the wizard. Wuldor is a Tolkein-inspired planet and its inhabitants should be dressed as in the many fighting fantasy books and comics.

Set: The first scene is a barren landscape, then moves to the royal palace on Wuldor, then to Don's bedroom on Earth. The author states that to ensure quick scene changes it is best not to have elaborate sets, and that if there is a cyclorama, different coloured 'skies' for Earth and Wuldor are effective.

Cast: M6 F1 (with doubling). Extras.
EARTH: Bryn Masters, our hero. Don Glastonbury, his friend. Hash Glastonbury, Don's father. Daisy Glastonbury, Don's mother. Shaun, another friend. WULDOR: Prince Erfa, played by the same actor as Bryn. King Fruma, his father; very old. Dwimor, a wizard. Royal Guards. Attendants.

Playing time: 24 minutes.

SCENE A

A barren landscape

The lighting is dim. Sinister pulsating music

Prince Erfa appears striding cautiously, looking to L to R. He looks like a fighting fantasy hero, wearing red boots and loin-cloth/trunks, a belt made of gold discs and a collar of the same design. He holds a sword at the ready

Two warriors enter from the opposite side, barring his path. He stops. Two more appear behind him, then another two surround him completely. They brandish fearsome weapons. The music builds up in pace and excitement. They attack. Using cunning, skill and strength, Erfa defeats them all

He limps off, wounded

The Lights fade to Black-out

SCENE B

The royal palace

A fanfare, followed by ceremonial music

Guards and Attendants lead in a procession. Two thrones are placed. King Fruma enters last of all and sits on the throne. All grovel to the King who is very old and walks with a stick

Fruma I sent for the prince half an hour ago. Why is he not in attendance?

The Guards and Attendants look at each other nervously

Well?
Guard 1 His royal highness, the Prince Erfa, is not in the palace, your Majesty.

The King rises and approaches the Guard

Fruma Not in the palace? Has there been a thorough search?
Guard 1 Yes, your Majesty. Parties of your Majesty's guards are seeking him through the city.
Fruma He was supposed to be under supervision fifty-three hours a day. I entrusted him to the court magician's care. Where is Dwimor, the old wizard? Summon him.
Guard 1 Summon Dwimor, the old wizard!

This is echoed by voices in the distance. Fruma turns towards his throne

Dwimor is sitting on the throne gazing into a crystal ball

Fruma Dwimor! (*To the audience*) The old wizard.
Dwimor Pardon me, your Majesty. I have been observing emanations from another world at the end of the galaxy. Fascinating.

Dwimor hands the crystal ball to Fruma for him to look at. We hear the "Neighbours" theme tune. The King is impatient

Fruma Dwimor! You were entrusted with the care of Prince Erfa. He cannot be found. If anything has happened to him ...

Dwimor He is safe.

Fruma You know where he is?

Dwimor No, I was just trying to reassure you.

Fruma Well, you failed. If anything has happened to my son, you will pay for it with your life!

Dwimor This is really most unfair, your Majesty.

Fruma You're a wizard, aren't you? Use some hocus-pocus and find him.

Dwimor If I may say so, your Majesty, that is typical of the attitude of the general public towards the necromantic arts.

Fruma How dare you refer to me as the general public!

Dwimor Magic is a deep and difficult branch of learning. It is not just a matter of hocus-pocus.

Fruma Off with his head! That's it! I've had enough of his incompetence. Off with his head! Guards! Take him away!

Dwimor But, your Majesty——

Fruma No. No. No. No. No. Don't explain. You failed. You die. Guards!

Dwimor It's not my fault. Take your hands off me or I'll turn you into toads.

Fruma Take him away.

Dwimor No. No. Spare me! A few hours with my books and I'll tell you exactly where he is. It's the ingredients. You can't get the ingredients for the spells these days. I mean when did you last see a bat's wing in the grocer's? Be honest. They're a protected species. What am I supposed to do?

Prince Erfa limps in

Erfa What's all the fuss?

Dwimor However, as you're so concerned, I have brought him back to the palace as you see. (*He releases himself from the Guards and takes back the crystal ball*) I only wish you had a little more faith in me, your Majesty. The prince is quite safe in my charge. I know exactly what he is doing at all times and protect him from all danger.

Erfa limps to the throne

Erfa I was attacked by six mysterious warriors.

Fruma What!

Dwimor As I knew of course, your Majesty. There was no real danger.

Erfa They tried to kill me.

Dwimor Ha ha ha ha ha ha.

Fruma What are you laughing at? My son is nearly killed and you laugh!

Dwimor Well, if we didn't laugh we'd have to cry I always say.

Fruma Dwimor! I don't think you appreciate the situation. Prince Erfa is my *only* child. The heir to my kingdom. I am four hundred and eighty-seven years old.

Dwimor Your Majesty is eternally youthful.

Fruma If anything happens to my son, then when I die, who will succeed to the throne?

Dwimor Your loyal subjects pray daily for your continued health, your Majesty.

Fruma Who will succeed to the throne?

Dwimor Your wicked brother Snithan.

The Guards spring to attention and look around threateningly

Fruma Exactly. These warriors who attacked you, Erfa. Were they sent by Snithan?

Erfa They didn't say.

Dwimor They were probably just marauding brigands, your Majesty, not expecting a royal prince to be walking alone in the wastelands of Scard.

Fruma Why *do* you disobey my instructions and leave the safety of the palace grounds alone?

Erfa Oh, Father, sometimes I feel that this place is a prison to me. My gold chains and rich jewels are like shackles binding me. Despite all our power and riches I sometimes envy the ordinary subjects of the kingdom. Yes, Father, I have rank, I have honour, but there are times when I would change if I could. Times when I dream of no longer being a prince and a hero. No longer looked up to and admired for my strength, my nobility, my virtue and my beauty, but instead, this is my dream, to be—ordinary.

Fruma Ordinary!

Erfa Yes, Father, ordinary—because an ordinary man, Father, has something worth far more than gold. He has freedom. True freedom—something I fear that I shall never know. (*He hangs his head in a tragic pose*)

Fruma Freedom! You can have freedom. You can go anywhere you want. You can do anything you want. You have *carte blanche.*

Fruma takes two Guards by their arms and stations one on each side of Erfa

These two *ordinary* people, however, will lose their heads if they let you out of their sight.

The Guards look very alarmed and close in on Erfa even further

And now I have affairs of state to attend to.

Pause

I wish to leave.

The others look at each other, puzzled

Dwimor Is something detaining your Majesty?
Fruma The fanfare. I'm the king. I can't leave without the fanfare.

Everyone bustles about. Fanfare, followed by ceremonial music

  Fruma and most of the Guards process out

Two Guards remain with Erfa. Dwimor is looking into his crystal ball

Dwimor Your highness, I did not wish to alarm the king your father, but those warriors who attacked you were indeed soldiers of your wicked Uncle Snithan.

Erfa walks to one side. The Guards and Dwimor follow

Erfa My own uncle wants to kill me? Tell me, Dwimor. You have lived long. Tell me about Snithan. Many times I have asked my father. He will not speak of it. Why does my uncle live in exile in the mountains of Snutz?

Erfa walks. They follow

Dwimor In the twenty-fourth century, when your father and his brother were young men, each of them fell in love, as young men will.

Erfa blushes. He walks. The Guards follow

As fate would have it, they both fell in love with the same beautiful and enchanting maiden. Both wooed but she had eyes only for your father. The marriage was arranged and there was joy throughout the kingdom. But there was no joy in your uncle's heart. Jealousy and bitterness were effecting a change in your noble uncle's demeanour. It was as if his disappointment in love drove all the goodness out of his head and left there only evil and a thirst for revenge.

Erfa walks. The Guards don't follow. They are hanging on Dwimor's every word. He motions to them. They follow Erfa

The day of the royal wedding drew near. All was prepared. Then, two days before the ceremony was to take place, the bride—vanished.
Erfa What do you mean?
Dwimor She disappeared. Could not be found. When her maid came to wake her the bed was empty.
Erfa Had she been murdered? Had my uncle ... ?
Dwimor He was, of course, suspected. Your father had no doubt that his brother had kidnapped or murdered the bride. Snithan would say nothing. Had he not been a

royal prince he would have been tortured to make him speak but as it was ... Your father exiled him to the ancient palace in the mountains of Snutz. He may never return on pain of death. What became of the bride has never been discovered. Many years later your father married your mother, our dear late queen.

Erfa And Uncle Snithan?

Dwimor There are always rumours that he plots his revenge. Spies have been caught in the kingdom but little is heard of him.

Erfa Why do I not lead an army into the mountains of Snutz and put an end to his evil schemes?

Dwimor Your father would never allow it. Your life is too valuable to put at risk.

Erfa My safety! Always my safety! I cannot bear these restrictions.

Erfa attacks the Guards who flinch, but stay close

Dwimor But the attack today, your highness. You uncle plans to kill you and if he failed today he will try again soon.

Erfa I am not afraid.

Dwimor Very commendable, your highness, but if you are killed, I will be executed and I do not share your royal courage.

Erfa I don't care, Dwimor. I will accept no further restrictions.

Dwimor But, your highness, I offer you freedom.

Erfa Freedom?

Dwimor The chance to be ... ordinary—as you wished.

Erfa Explain. I don't understand.

Dwimor One moment.

Dwimor takes the crystal ball and hands it to the Guards. He points at it. They look. We hear the title music from the children's TV show "Rainbow". They are riveted. Dwimor and Erfa step away from them

Your uncle seems determined to murder you. He is cunning. We may be unable to prevent him. The best way would be to catch him in the act.

Erfa Of murdering me?

Dwimor Exactly.

Erfa I thought you would not risk my life.

Dwimor I will not. I will risk the life of Brynmor.

Erfa Brynmor? Who is Brynmor?

Dwimor He is from another world. Let me explain. As you know, my receivers (*he points to the crystal ball*) intercept transmissions from other worlds, other dimensions. It was in this way that I discovered Brynmor. Look at this holographic image. (*He shows Erfa a piece of plastic*) Brynmor!

Erfa He looks exactly like me.

Dwimor Now you will see my plan. I use my necromantic skills to exchange you with him until your uncle's plans come to fruition and we can defeat him. You will have a taste of freedom. Brynmor is not a prince in his world. He is what you wished to be—an ordinary person.

Erfa Has he agreed to this?

Dwimor I was thinking of making it a surprise.

Erfa You're probably right. But will I not seem very out of place in this other world?

Dwimor That is the problem. Time is short—not long enough for detailed study. Take this volume and learn what you can about the people of Earth. The data banks show that it is by the man deemed to be their greatest writer. (*He gives Erfa a book*)

Erfa *William Shakespeare. The Complete Works.* Dwimor, I will start at once.

Erfa runs out. He comes back and whistles at the Guards. They follow him out. Dwimor takes the crystal ball and leaves to the title music of "Last of the Summer Wine"

SCENE C

Don's bedroom

Darkness

Hash Glastonbury is on a step-ladder changing the light bulb. Shaun is sitting at the table where a role-playing boardgame is in progress

Hash OK, Donovan, you can turn it on now.

The Lights come up

Don enters

That's the last one. The whole house is now fitted with these new low energy light bulbs. Just as bright but they use less power. That should ease the demands on the generator. I hope the interruption didn't spoil your game.

Shaun No, Mr Glastonbury, we can't carry on until Bryn arrives.

Hash Mr Glastonbury! Shaun, we're all on first name terms in this house.

Shaun I don't know your first name, sir.

Hash Sir! The name is Hash. You can call me Hash.

Shaun That's an unusual name.

Hash More of a nickname really.

Don His real name's Nelson.

Hash I never liked it even as a child. Military associations. Bad vibrations. And then when it came to the sixties—Grosvenor Square, Aldermaston—well, I think your name is so much a part of your essential spirit, don't you?

Shaun Oh, yes.

Hash So some of my friends started calling me Hash.

Don (*meaningfully*) For some reason.

Hash For some reason, yes. And the name has stuck. It seemed to suit my—lifestyle. You can hardly imagine someone called Nelson being a Friend of the Earth, can you?

Daisy enters with a plate of cakes, drinks, etc., singing "White Rabbit" by Jefferson Airplane

Daisy Here you are. I baked some more of those fairy cakes.

Don Well don't let Shaun eat any. He started having hallucinations last time.

Hash Is this the nettle wine?

Daisy No, it's—daffodil.

Shaun and Don gag on theirs

Hash Daffodil? It must be years since we had this, Daisy. You know, Daisy, daffodil always reminds me of the first time we met.

Daisy Stonehenge.

Hash Summer solstice nineteen sixty-nine.

Hash and Daisy sing a line from "Aquarius" from the musical Hair. *They continue singing selections from the Flower Power songbook during the following*

Don Oh no. I hate it when they get like this.

Shaun And we haven't even started on the fairy cakes yet. (*He picks one up*)

Don Put that down.

Shaun Oh, Don.

Don (*gesturing towards the game*) You came here for an adventure.

Shaun These cakes *are* an adventure.

Don Sometimes, Shaun, I think you're a closet hippie. You'd *like* a permissive society, wouldn't you?

Shaun Well, they look happy. My parents are miserable, worrying about their share portfolios.

Hash and Daisy are now on "Good Morning Starshine" from the musical Hair

Don Isn't this a song from *Hair*?

Shaun I don't know. Why?

Don That usually means they start taking their clothes off.

Shaun Wow! You mean right here in front of us?

Don Anywhere. I swear I will *never* forget my tenth birthday party.

Doorbell

That'll be Bryn. Go and let him in, Shaun, while I deal with this situation.

Shaun goes out, sneaking a fairy cake as he does so

Mum, Dad. Will you please stop this?

Hash What's the matter, Donovan? We're enjoying ourselves.

Don Other people's parents don't still live in the nineteen sixties. What's the matter with you?

Daisy Donovan, your father and I believed in peace and love in the nineteen sixties and we still believe in them in the nineteen nineties. You don't change your beliefs according to fashion, like clothes. (*She looks at Hash's clothes*)

Don But you haven't changed your clothes either! Don't you realize it's embarrassing when my friends come round here and you're dressed up in caftans and flares and bells? How do you think I feel when they come round and see you like this? Don't you realize you look ridiculous?

Shaun and Bryn enter

Bryn is on his skateboard and executes one or two clever moves. He wears a "Blue Peter" version of Erfa's costume. The gold belt and necklace are replaced by milk bottle tops strung together. The arm pieces are now badly painted washing-up liquid bottles. Instead of Erfa's boots Bryn wears a pair of wellies. Everyone stares at him

Hash Er ... I think I hear the goat calling me. I'd better go and attend to it.

Hash goes

Daisy Yes, we'll leave you to your games, boys. Donovan, I didn't realize you had such interesting friends. (*She hands Bryn a fairy cake*) Have fun.

Daisy goes out singing "I Can Hear the Grass Grow" by the Move

Don stands staring at Bryn. Bryn smiles back and eats the cake

Bryn Are we ready, then? Do you like the costume? I copied it from one of those books you lent me. I had to improvise a bit. I thought it would help us to get into the spirit of it if we wore the appropriate costume. Why are you staring at me like that? Is it the swimming trunks? I haven't got any red ones. Apart from that, though, what do you think?

Shaun It's very nice, isn't it, Don?

Don stares, walks over to the drinks and pours himself a daffodil wine

Why don't we get on with the game. Come on, Don.

They all sit at the table

Don Are those milk bottle tops?
Bryn Yeah.
Don And these?
Bryn Washing-up liquid.
Don And wellies.
Bryn That was an inspiration.
Don Did your parents see you going out like that?
Bryn They're away for the weekend. Second honeymoon they call it.
Shaun Where have they gone? Somewhere romantic?
Bryn Yes. Abergele. So I'm on my own till Tuesday.
Don I thought you weren't very keen on the idea of these role-playing games?
Bryn That was before I came here yesterday. Now I realize that this is what I've wanted all my life.
Don To dress up in milk bottle tops and wellies?
Bryn No. To be a hero. I know I'm good at skateboarding and football and swimming—and cross-country running—and basketball—and gymnastics—but that's not enough, is it?
Don Er ... no.
Bryn Being a sports hero is not like being a real hero and fighting evil and defeating injustice, is it?
Shaun ⎫
             ⎬ (*together*) Er ... no.
Don   ⎭
Bryn But with these games you can kind of act out your fantasies, can't you?
Shaun ⎫
             ⎬ (*together*) Er ... yes.
Don   ⎭

Shaun and Don turn their attention to the table. Black-out

> *Bryn leaves in the darkness to make a quick costume change. When ready he appears as Erfa*

Shaun I think your father's everlasting low energy light bulb has gone.
Don Either that or the generator's packed in again.
Shaun No. It can't be the generator. I can still hear your mother's Grateful Dead record on the stereo.
Don I think my father left the other bulb over here somewhere. I'll see if I can find it and put it in. Will you turn it off at the switch, Shaun?
Shaun If I can find the switch.

There are noises of scraping chairs, stumbling, collisions, curses

I don't know how you cope with this happening all the time.

Don Have you got the switch?
Shaun I think so.

Click. Then very loud buzzing, clattering, siren noises

Don Turn it off. Turn it off!
Shaun What was that?
Don Well, it wasn't the light switch. It was my Star Trek Klingon destructor ray gun.
Shaun This must be the light switch.
Don Are you sure?

There is another strange noise. This is Dwimor's spell operating but they do not realize this. How could they?

Shaun What was that? Your Doctor Who Dalek disintegration beam?
Don I don't know. I haven't got anything that sounds like that. For goodness' sake hurry up and find the light switch.
Shaun That's it, definitely. You know, there's something spooky about your bedroom, Don. I haven't forgotten the last time.
Don OK. Switch on.

The Lights come up. Erfa is sitting exactly as Bryn was

Don Good. You've gone very quiet Bryn. Afraid of the dark?
Erfa Good-morrow, my friends.
Shaun You're not going to *talk* heroically too, are you?
Erfa I bring thee greetings from my native land.
Don OK. OK. If it helps you get into role.
Shaun Now, where were we? Oh yes, this malignant troll. Hey, does he remind you of anyone?
Don (*looking at a book*) No. Who?
Shaun Creepy Westmorland, our new maths teacher.
Don Oh yeah. I see what you mean.
Shaun Do you know what he did yesterday? Matthew Tiler fired a pellet at the blackboard while Westmorland was writing on it and he turned round and blamed me. Put me on detention next Tuesday. I'm not going though.
Don If you don't, you'll get put on report.
Shaun It's not fair.
Erfa Come take up arms against this Westmorland
  'Gainst foul injustice let thy hand be set.
Shaun Hit him, you mean? I don't think that would be a good idea.
Erfa What, shall we let this tyrant hold such sway?
  Such men have power but by our consent.
  Why shouldst thou pay thus for another's sin?
  In noble combat prove thy innocence.

Don Forget it. Let's get on with the game.
Erfa (*standing*) Thou thinkst that being young thou still hast time
   Time when in years to come thou art a man
   But courage is a plant that groweth not
   Without it be exposed to healthful sun
   Close hid, young shoots will wither and so die.
Don He's gone. It's these damned fairy cakes.
Shaun I don't think so. Look. (*He points at Erfa's clothing*)
Don (*embarrassed*) What?
Shaun They were blue. Now they're red.
Erfa If thou expect'st when that thou art a man
   To call upon a courage never tried
   No trusty oak of valour wilt thou find
   Weak rootless sapling courage will be thine.
Shaun And look at the belt. It's gold. What happened to the milk bottle tops?
Don And where are the wellies?
Shaun Something spooky's happening again!
Erfa If this vile Westmorland hath shamèd thee
   Let not thy vengeance wait upon thy doubt
   And if my arm be strong, thy cause be right
   Come follow me to Westmorland this night.

Erfa produces a sword from behind the table, raises it high and strides out

Don Where did he get that from? We'd better follow him.
Shaun I'm never coming to your house again!

Shaun picks up Bryn's skateboard and they chase after Erfa

THE BURSTON DRUM
by Ellen Dryden

Based on a true story set in the village of Burston between 1911 and 1914, this musical play tells of the pupils' support and eventual strike when their dedicated teachers, Kitty and Tom Higdon, are unfairly dismissed. This scene is a sub-plot conflict between the pupils. Kitty has won the hearts of all the village children and has to defend the integrity of a young boy, Harry, against two new pupils, the unloved orphans, Gertie and Ethel, who are under the thumb of their unreliable foster-mother, Mrs Philpot.

Set: The setting is flexible: initially the playground area, and in the second scene, the schoolroom. Period: between 1911 and 1914.

Cast: M1 F3, 4 boys 8 girls. Extras.
Kitty Higdon, small, energetic, bright-eyed. Tom Higdon, her husband, big and burly; younger. Violet, a lively pupil; 13. PUPILS AT BURSTON VILLAGE SCHOOL: Marjorie, Rosie, Daisy, Hetty, Ivy, Harry (the accused), Arthur, George, Billy, Gertie and Ethel. Mrs Philpot, their foster-mother, a very unpleasant character. Mrs Potter, Violet's mother. Villagers.

Playing time: 17 minutes.

Children (*off, shouting*) It's playtime!

The children run on

They disperse to various parts of the stage to begin their playground games in groups. Harry and his friends play marbles, Rosie and her friends hopscotch. Hetty and Marjorie come downstage and begin to sort through their bag of material scraps. Violet moves centre to address the audience directly

Violet We thought it was marvellous—Mr Higdon coming top of the poll and Mr Eland right at the bottom. But that was the start of the real trouble. Grown-ups spend a lot of their time telling us to be unselfish and sporting and see fair play—but most of them don't practise what they preach. Mr Eland got all his friends—his wife, another vicar, the farmers—on the School Management Board. There was only Mr Witherley from the Parish Council to stick up for Mr and Mrs Higdon—

and us! Two parsons, and a parson's wife out of six Council School Managers. Mr Eland went off to Switzerland then for a holiday. We didn't miss him much.

Violet runs back to join Hetty and Marjorie, as one girl, Gertie, who has been on her own throughout, wandering from group to group, pauses by the hopscotch players

Gertie Can I join in?
Rosie Not this time. When we've finished this round.

Gertie wanders off

Daisy What did you say that for? We don't want her at all.
Rosie Well, she's new. She might be nice.
Daisy Not coming from old Ma Philpot's she couldn't be!

They get on with their game. Gertie wanders through the boys' marbles game

Harry Watch out big feet!
George Don't step on that or I'll scrag you!
Billy Go and get in somebody else's way, smelly drawers!
Gertie (*kicking aside the marbles*) Stupid game anyway!

She runs off out of their way, as they scrabble to get their marbles back. Gertie crosses downstage, where Violet, Hetty and Marjorie are in earnest conversation over the scraps of material, which they immediately hide away as Gertie draws near

Gertie Hallo.
The Others Hallo.

There is a pause. Gertie will not go away. She points at a scrap of ribbon that Marjorie has not pushed fully out of sight

Gertie What are you doing?
Hetty Oh. Nothing.
Gertie Yes you are. What have you got that pile of rags for? I saw you hiding them up your sleeve.
Violet It's not rags. It's bits of material.
Gertie What you got them in the playground for?
Marjorie We can't say.
Gertie Why not?
Marjorie Because it's a secret.
Gertie You've pinched 'em. From the sewing cupboard.
Violet No! We haven't.
Gertie Well, what you doing with them then? I'll tell Miss.

Violet No you won't. You won't say anything to Miss.

Gertie Yes I will. If you don't tell me——

Hetty Well—we're not going to. So there!

Gertie I think you're all horrible. Nobody lets me join in. Nobody talks to me—or — or anything.

Violet Well, you've only just come here. Nobody's going to bother with you if you go telling tales on your second day.

Gertie Miss said you were to be nice to me and Ethel and make us feel welcome.

Violet Well we will, but not if you're spiteful.

Gertie Don't like it here anyway.

Hetty Go on. It's better than Barnardo's, isn't it?

Gertie Not much.

Marjorie Well. You've got to get used to it.

Gertie That's what Mrs Philpot says ... What *are* you doing with those bits of rag?

Violet If we tell you do you promise not to say anything?

Gertie Cross my heart.

Violet Well. Don't say anything at all. Not to anybody. We're going to make a Christmas present for the Governess.

Gertie Is that all?

Marjorie (*crossly*) Yes it is. We want to make her a really nice one—We don't know whether to make her a pot-holder with this bit of flannel—we could cut it out like a flower and stuff it with these scraps and embroider flowers on it in lazy-daisy stitch——

Violet Or we could make a pincushion with this bit of blue velvet and bind it with this ribbon——

Hetty I think the pincushion would be nicest.

Gertie Why don't you do both?

Violet Not enough scraps.

Gertie Well. I think it's peculiar making presents for your teachers. We didn't do that at Barnardo's.

Hetty Are you stopping here? Or going back to Barnardo's?

Gertie Stopping. Me and Ethel are adopted now. I hate Ethel, I never liked her at Barnardo's and now I've got to live with her all the time. We've got to do what Mrs Philpot says or she'll send us back.

Hetty Did she say that?

Gertie Well, it's obvious isn't it?

Marjorie I thought you wouldn't mind going back?

Gertie Not getting *sent* back though.

Hetty Ma Philpot won't send you back. She gets paid for you. And she's the meanest woman in the village.

Violet And the dirtiest.

Marjorie And the worst-tempered.

They giggle together. Gertie looks depressed

Hetty Does she give you proper food?
Gertie Ye-es. Well. Sometimes.
Marjorie Do you like her?
Gertie Not much.
Hetty My brother knocked a ball into her garden and she came and walloped him
    with the copper stick. And she never gave him his ball back.
Gertie Ethel says she does hit you a lot ... a bit, I mean. But Mr Eland says we've got
    to be good girls because she's taken us in out of the goodness of her heart like a
    good Christian.

*The others roar with laughter at this. Harry, playing marbles on the opposite side of
the stage, leaps up with a cry of triumph*

Violet She never goes near the church.
Gertie That boy over there—with the whip and top. What's his name?
Marjorie Harry Oates. Why?
Gertie Where does he live?
Hetty Down the Glebe, why?
Gertie Nothing ... Me and Ethel ... we were talking to him ... (*She falters and stops*)
Hetty Where *is* Ethel?
Gertie Erm. She's got a cold. And she's helping Mrs Philpot with the washing.
Ivy (*overhearing them*) No she's not. She's coming down the lane. Look. (*She
    points*)

*Mrs Philpot comes in, dragging Ethel with her. Ethel is terrified and very reluctant
to be brought in like this. Mrs Philpot is an energetic, aggressive woman*

Gertie Oh no!! (*She darts off upstage and hides behind a group of the others, as far
    away from Mrs Philpot as possible*)

*Mrs Philpot marches into the centre of all the children and glares round. The children
all stop what they are doing and stare fascinated*

Mrs Philpot Gertie Stearness!!! Come here. I want to talk to you.

Gertie stays put

Gertie. Did you hear me? I know you're there, if you don't come out at once it'll be
the worse for you. Gertie!! I'm warning you. I shan't tell you again!! Gertie!!!

*Ethel gestures to Gertie, who is still trying to hide. Gertie, defeated, creeps out and
goes and stands beside her. She pinches her viciously, and Ethel cries out and digs
her elbow into Gertie's side*

Oh there you are. About time too. And you can stop that or I'll fetch you one. (*She suddenly changes her tone and positively coos at the girls*) Now girls ... Gertie, Ethel, my little chicks. You mustn't be frightened. I want you to point him out to me.

The girls look at each other, worried, but do not say or do anything. Mrs Philpot's tone hardens slightly

Come on, Gertie. You remember. What you told me. You know why I'm here.
Gertie What?
Mrs Philpot (*the sweetness begins to vanish*) The disgusting rude boy.

During the following scene, the villagers, attracted by the noise, begin to gather at the edges of the playground

Gertie (*mulishly*) What boy?
Mrs Philpot (*dangerously*) Don't be silly, Gertie. (*She bends down and seizes Gertie viciously by the arms*) Come on, now. You know who I mean. The rude filthy boy that did that disgusting thing in front of you and Ethel. Ethel knows what I mean, don't you dear?

Ethel nods

Have you forgotten last night, Gertie? (*She grabs hold of Gertie's hair. With each sentence she gives it a vicious little tug*) How you told me about that horrible rude boy. How frightened you were. How you cried. How you couldn't bring yourself to tell me. How I looked after you like a mother. How I cuddled you and made it better. How you told me everything. Now, I want you to point him out.
Gertie Who?
Mrs Philpot (*through gritted teeth*) The rude boy. The rude boy, you little—Ethel knows. You speak to her, Ethel.

She pushes Gertie at Ethel and the two whisper together. They look worriedly at Mrs Philpot

I'm waiting. Which boy was it? Gertie!!

Gertie and Ethel whisper together again and look round at the circle of children

Gertie Him.

Gertie points at Harry, who looks puzzled

It was him.
Mrs Philpot Are you sure?
Ethel Yes. Yes. It was him. Yesterday. In the playground, it was him.

Harry What do you mean? What are you talking about?

Mrs Philpot You filthy, horrible, disgusting little devil. (*She seizes him and drags him* c) I'm not letting you get away with this. Decent clean-minded people come to this school. These poor innocent children aren't used to that sort of filth you know.

Somewhat unconvincingly she gathers the two girls to her. They stand quite still, afraid to pull away

Harry What are you talking about? I haven't done nothing. Do you know what she's on about?

Boys No, dunno, she's barmy!

Gertie Yes. You know what you did. By the tree. Over there ... (*Her voice fades away*)

Harry (*shouting*) I don't know what you're on about!! What am I supposed to have done?

Mrs Philpot Don't you try to play the innocent with me, young man. You know what you did. And it was filthy!! Don't you try to make these poor little things say out loud in front of everybody what a disgusting thing you did.

Harry (*beginning to worry a little*) I haven't done anything. Honest. Honest, missis, I don't know what you're talking about.

Mrs Philpot Gertie. Ethel. Tell him.

Gertie He ... was ... rude ... over there ...

Ethel Yes. That's right. It was him.

Harry It wasn't. I didn't do nothing. It wasn't me. I don't know what it was I done. Anyway it wasn't me.

Mrs Philpot Yes it was you, you filthy little beast. You're going to be punished. I'll see you don't get away with this.

All the rest of the village enters. Finally, the whole cast is on stage, including Tom, Kitty, and the Elands

The children form a group round Violet and Harry, Gertie and Ethel are in the middle, worried and frightened, Mrs Philpot is LC

Harry It's a lie. I never done anything.

George No that's right. That old bag's just out to cause trouble.

Arthur (*angrily to Gertie and Ethel*) Liars!! Why don't you go back to Barnardo's where you belong. We don't want you here telling your lies, do we boys!

Children No, no!

Violet No. Shut up a minute, Arthur. Gertie. Ethel. Come here a minute.

With an anxious look at Mrs Philpot the girls go to her

Is it true? Did that really happen? Or are you just saying what *she* told you to?

Mrs Philpot And who's she? The cat's mother? You cheeky little hussy! (*She raises her hand to strike Violet*)

Mrs Potter Don't you touch my Violet!

Mrs Philpot (*to Violet*) I'll have a few words to say about you as well!!

Violet (*urgently*) Gertie! You'll get Harry into awful trouble. You wouldn't do that—you didn't even know who he was till I told you. You asked me——

Mrs Philpot Gertie. Ethel. Come here! I'm waiting.

Gertie We don't have to listen to you, Violet Potter.

Ethel Teacher's pet!

Gertie }
Ethel } (*together*) Yes it was. It was him!

Harry }
Arthur } (*together*) No they're telling lies!!

The children's chorus hurries off stage in all directions, full of concern, followed by the villagers. Mrs Philpot glares at Violet and Harry, and drags Gertie and Ethel off stage with her, as Violet and Harry run hurriedly off in the opposite direction

The empty schoolroom

On the blackboard is written, "It is February the 27th. It is very cold."

The children enter and stand silently behind their desks, heads bowed and hands clasped in front of them. Gertie and Ethel creep in at the back

Tom and Kitty enter

Tom }
Kitty } (*together*) Good-morning, everyone.

Class Good-morning, Mrs Higdon. Good-morning, Mr Higdon.

Kitty Now. Before we get on with our morning's work we have a nasty little problem to clear up. Gertie. Ethel. Harry. Step forward please.

The three named do so

Gertie. Now you have made some very serious accusations against Harry. I want you to tell us all—the whole school, what it was you had to say about him. Ethel. You too.

Harry Please, Miss, I didn't do nothing.

Kitty Anything. No, Harry, not yet. You will have your turn to speak in a minute. Well, Gertie, what have you to say?

Pause

Come along. We must never be afraid to speak the truth. And if we are speaking the truth we should be able to speak it in front of the whole world.

Gertie I can't, Miss.

Kitty What did you say?

Gertie I can't, Miss.

Kitty Why not? You have already said these things about Harry to your foster-mother and to the Reverend Eland. We can't have these stories flying around. If Harry was as rude as you say he was he must apologize and be punished.

Harry Miss, I never ... I mean I didn't——

Kitty (*stopping him with a gesture*) All right, Harry ... Ethel?

Ethel It was her, Miss. I didn't say it ... Not at first. It was Gertie.

Gertie looks daggers at Ethel but cannot do anything else in front of everyone

Kitty Gertie. You had only been at the school for one day when this incident was said to have occurred. Do you mean to tell me that on your second day here Harry found you out and was deliberately rude to you? After I had asked the whole class to be kind and welcoming to you. That doesn't sound like Harry to me.

Gertie He did, Miss. It was him. Honest. (*Viciously*) Wasn't it, Ethel?

Ethel I think so ... In the playground ... I saw ... (*She falters and stops*)

Tom has been checking the register which he now shows to Kitty. Kitty takes the register and Tom returns to his seat

Kitty Gertie. Ethel. Which day was this?

Gertie Wednesday, Miss.

Kitty Ethel?

Ethel Yes, Miss, Wednesday.

Kitty Are you sure?

Gertie
Ethel } (*together*) Yes, Miss.

Kitty Quite sure.

Gertie Yes, Miss. I know it was Wednesday because — because ... (*She falters and stops*)

Ethel eagerly takes up the tale

Ethel (*triumphantly*) Mr Eland came to talk to Mrs Philpot after choir practice. He always comes on a Wednesday!

Kitty Come here. All three of you. Look. In the register. That Wednesday. You were here, Gertie. There's your big black tick. And yours, Ethel. You were both here. But look. That big red O by Harry's name. That means Harry wasn't here when I called the register. And he wasn't late. Look there's another red O in the afternoon. Harry didn't come to school at all that day.

Harry (*radiant*) No, Miss, I didn't. I didn't have no boots. There was a big hole in them. My dad had to mend them when he came in from work. I couldn't come to school. I wasn't here, Miss, I said I didn't do it.

The children cheer. Kitty silences them with a gesture

Kitty Well, Gertie? Ethel?

Ethel (*turning savagely on Gertie*) You! It's your fault. I didn't want to do it. You see—he wasn't here that day. What did you want to go and say Wednesday for?

Gertie Shut up, stupid. Now look what you've done. She'll wallop us now.

Kitty Who's "she"? Do you mean me? Because I certainly am not going to wallop you, I don't believe it ever did any good.

Ethel No, Miss. Mrs Philpot. She said she'd lather us with the copper stick if we didn't——

Gertie Shut up ... She's always hitting us, Miss.

Kitty That's enough. Now listen to me. At the end of school today you are to come with me to Harry's house and you are to tell his mother that you made it all up and you are very sorry for telling lies about him and you will never do it again.

Gertie Miss. If we're late home we get the stick.

Kitty I shall be there to explain what has happened. All right, children. All stand. Harry as you are not the criminal we feared, you and the boys can clear up the classroom before we go on our walk.

Harry (*wreathed in smiles*) Yes, Miss.

Kitty All right, girls. Off we go. Boys. I shall expect to see you in a very few minutes.

Tom Don't worry they'll be right behind you. All right, boys?

The girls go out with Kitty

Tom watches with an amused smile

The boys sweep Harry out in triumph leaving Tom alone on stage

DREAMS OF ANNE FRANK
by Bernard Kops

This is a new version of the famous Anne Frank story: how two Jewish families hid from the Nazis for two years in a cramped Amsterdam attic and the fantasy world the adolescent Anne Frank created to escape her incarceration. In these final scenes, the tragedy is heightened because the end of the Second World War is in sight. Anne's dreams carry her out of the attic and make her believe that Hitler is dead, and that she and Peter have discovered their love for each other.

Set: The attic, the place of hiding in Amsterdam, but in her dreams, Anne moves out of the attic into an empty square, outside the Royal Palace. When they are all captured, the scene becomes a sort of box-car, enveloped in fog: a train scene. Period: 1944.

Cast: M4 F4.
Anne Frank. Otto Frank, her father. Edith Frank, her mother. Peter Van Daan, 16. Mrs Van Daan, his mother. Mr Van Daan, his father. Margot, Anne's older sister. Mr Dussel, a dentist.

Playing time: 15 minutes.

SCENE A

Everyone is seated for a meal in the attic

Edith Come and get it! Tulip bulb and potato soup!
Peter Dreams are over. Back to who we are. Back to where we are.
Anne Amsterdam. August the fourth, nineteen forty-four.

Air-raid outside

Edith The war is nearly over and we shall be free.
Anne Free!
Edith What?
Anne Nothing. (*She smiles, trying to hide her foreboding*)

Edith Tell me the truth. What do you see?

Anne I see peace. Perfect and beautiful peace. And I love you both, forever. (*She hugs her mother and father*)

Edith   ⎱ (*together*) ⎰ Soup! Soup! Who wants soup?
Mrs Van Daan   ⎰   ⎱ Lunchtime. Come and get it.

The others eat

Mrs Van Daan Join in, Anne! That's your trouble. You never join in.

Peter This soup is wonderful. Ugh!

Edith Lunch will do for supper tomorrow, so let's all have breakfast tonight.

Margot After this war and the end of this nightmare I want to go out into the streets of Amsterdam and kiss the very first handsome young man I meet and fall in love and get married and have five children.

Mrs Van Daan You'll be lucky.

Margot I've not given up hope. Where there's life there's hope. And I know that all this will soon be a thing of the past and we'll get on and live our lives to the full.

Peter Eat! That's my philosophy. Eat while you can. Live for the moment.

Anne Boys! All they think about. Their stomachs.

Peter is lost in eating. Anne goes to leave

Edith Where are you going, darling?

Anne I need fresh air. I need to escape. I need to see my beautiful city. Just once more. I need to stretch and breathe the sky.

Edith (*humouring her*) Yes, darling. Don't we all.

Anne tries the trap-door

Darling. What are you doing?

Anne The empty ballroom of dreams. (*She sings the chorus of "Dancing in the Dark"*)

Anne floats into an empty square. Amsterdam at night. There are searchlights and the crump of bombs

Come, bombs! Come, fire! Devour the Nazi monster. Even destroy my beloved Amsterdam if you have to.

Outside the Royal Palace. A man (Dussel) stalks her

Man What are you doing in the streets, child? In the middle of the night?

Anne Looking for my childhood.

Man But surely you want to grow up?

Anne Yes. But I'm afraid. I want life to go backwards.

Man Ah yes, I thought you were in pain. Can I tell you about my hobby? I am totally obsessed with military bands. I would follow any band, good or bad, to the ends of the earth and often do in my imagination. As soon as I get home I immediately start the military music on my radiogram. I know every march ever written, almost every band that ever played, their particular style. There in my living-room I march, back and forth, back and forth, every lunchtime, every night. It is a wonderful exercise and I can assure you it is a morally uplifting and spiritual experience. The Germans are a humane race, compassionate. I know you are afraid because of the things you have heard they have done or are about to do. A lot of this you can disregard. It is propaganda. I maintain that soon you will notice a big change. An occupying power is bound to take actions that seem draconian and excessively harsh early on. The Jews are merely an expediency, a scapegoat for our ambitions. It is almost understandable, even if a little painful. Open up. (*He has become Hitler and wants to probe into Anne's mouth*) Where's my scalpel?

Anne Here! (*She takes the knife from his white coat pocket and thrusts it into his stomach*)

Man Help me. Help me. Heil ―― (*He raises his arm, calling to her, but his cry becomes Hitler's fanatical call to his followers*) Heil! Heil!

Mass crowds shout "Heil!" in reply

Anne Hitler's dead. (*She is by the radio*)

Edith (*coming to Anne*) What are you doing up, this time of night?

Anne Mother! (*She whispers in Edith's ear*)

Edith What?

Anne It's true! It's true!

Edith What are you saying?

Anne again whispers in her ear

   How do you know?

Anne It must be true. It must be so. They announced it on the radio.

Edith It's wonderful! Wake up, everyone! It's wonderful!

Mrs Van Daan (*emerging from sleep*) What's happening?

Edith It's true. (*She whispers into Mrs Van Daan's ear*)

Mrs Van Daan Are you sure?

Edith It's true!

Mrs Van Daan How do you know?

Edith Anne heard it on the radio. It's official!

Mrs Van Daan kisses Edith and dances with her

Mrs Van Daan Wake up, everyone! Wake up. It's true. It's official.

One by one the rest emerge from sleep, yawning and still barely comprehending

All What is it? Is it the end of the world?
Mrs Van Daan It's wonderful. It's unbelievable. It's official.
Dussel Wait! How do we know it's true?
All Yes! How do we know? How do we know?
Edith It must be true. It must be so. She heard it on the radio.
Anne It must be true. It must be so. I heard it on the radio.

All now move ritualistically, building up to a climax, the words spurring them on. They all chant

Hitler Is Dead

All   Hitler is dead!
                    Hitler is dead!
                    Shot in the head.
                    Butchered in bed.
                    Maggots are crawling
                    Inside his head.
                    His eyeballs are jelly,
                    He's skewered through the belly.
                    He's mangled and minced
                    And we are convinced
                    That Hitler is dead.
                    Hitler is dead. Hitler is dead.
                    Strangled in bed.
                    Strangled in bed.
                    They've sawn off his thighs,
                    Sucked out his eyes.
                    Slugs in his sockets,
                    Rats in his pockets.
                    Battered and shattered,
                    Shattered and battered.
                    They've scattered his head,
                    His fingers, his toes,
                    His heart, his nose.
                    His fingers, his toes,
                    His heart, his nose.
                    Hitler is dead! Dead!
                    Dead! Dead!
                    Dead dead dead. DEAD!

At the end they are drained, shattered

SCENE B

Mr Van Daan Let's celebrate! I've been saving something special.

They laugh as Mr Van Daan brings out a bottle of wine from his secret hiding place

Dussel Are we sure? Who heard this news?
Anne I did. On the radio.
Mr Van Daan (*looking down through the trap-door*) Nothing's different in the street.
Dussel (*twiddling the radio*) Everything's the same. Nothing's new. It's not true.
Edith Anne, is it true?
Otto Is it true? Is it true?
Anne It must be true. He must be dead. I want him to be dead. Dad! Mummy! Please
   let him be dead.

Edith whispers to her husband

Mrs Van Daan Liar! Liar! How could you do this to us? (*Suddenly she attacks
   Anne, pulling her hair*)
Mr Van Daan (*trying to restrain his wife*) Angel face! Please!
Edith She's only a child. She's only a child! It was a joke. You understand jokes.
Mr Van Daan It was a bad joke, Anne. The time for jokes is over.

Anne is crying

Edith (*stroking Anne's hair*) Take no notice, darling. She means well but she's
   stupid ...
Mrs Van Daan Me? Stupid? Did you call me stupid?
Otto Silence! Or we'll be discovered.

They all start whispering

Mrs Van Daan This is the worst thing that ever happened to me. This dreaming,
   thinking and writing. It leads to trouble. It should be stopped. That girl should face
   reality.
Otto Anne, she's right. You must stop dreaming.
Anne Without dreams what are we?
Edith Anne! I understand. But we all have to grow up.
Anne Look what the grown-ups have done to this world. Hitler must be dead. He
   must be dead.
Mrs Van Daan (*angrily*) Peter! Stay away from her.

Peter Yes, Mother.
Otto Stay away from him.
Anne Yes, Father.
Mr Van Daan We mean it, young man! And go to bed.

All disperse, fading into the shadows as the Lights concentrate on Anne and Peter

Peter Yes, Father. I love you, Anne. Forever.
Anne I love you until the end of the world.
Peter And this is true and not a dream.
Anne But dreams are also true. The truth of your deep inner self.
Peter You're writing all this down, aren't you?
Anne Yes.
Peter Read your diary to me. Please. All of it. Now.
Anne No-one else must ever read my diary. My secrets. My truth.
Peter Am I in your diary?
Anne What do you think?
Peter Please show me your diary.
Anne Now?
Peter Now. Please.
Anne I must tell you this. I love you with this kiss.

They kiss

   At least we have this.
Peter At least we have this. I love you with this kiss.

They kiss again

Anne I would have loved a lifetime of this.

Anne opens her diary. A terrible wind blows. All the doors fly open. The diary flies out of her hand

   No. Not yet? I haven't finished yet.
                  Helping Hand!
                  Please help me.
                  Turn back the clock.
                  Save us in time.
Peter What's happening?
Anne We are betrayed.
Peter How? Who?

The door comes off its hinges. Smoke pours in. German voices are heard

Anne Does it matter now? We're going on a journey.

Suddenly we hear people rushing upstairs, shouting, spiralling, echoing voices

Voices Raus! Raus! Juden raus! Schnell! Schnell!

Menacing sounds drown everything. Then silence and blinding light

Anne Just as my world opens, it closes. Just as I stop being a child I stop being. In my beginning is my end.

Train sounds

   Night and fog. Night and fog.

Fog envelops them and in the darkness a thin light shines on all our people. They have become a mass, a sort of box-car. We concentrate on each face in turn

Mrs Van Daan Why?
Mr Van Daan Why?
Margot Why?
Edith Why?
Otto Why?
Peter Why?
Dussel Why?

SCENE C

The sound of trains wailing, chugging. The cast all wear yellow stars

Anne Dreams are over. The nightmare starts. Night and fog. Night and fog. Night and fog. (*Throughout this train scene she continues to repeat this litany*)
Dussel Why are humans doing this to humans? Why?
Mrs Van Daan Goodbye! Goodbye. Goodbye, Amsterdam.
Mr Van Daan Goodbye, world. Family. Friends.
Margot We didn't ask much from life. We just wanted to live it.
Edith Remember us. Bear witness.
Otto This is the end of the end of the end.
Margot Who will remember us? Who will know we were here?

They undress to reveal identical prison camp clothing

All   "Ani ma-amin
                          Ani ma-amin

> Ani ma-amin
> Be-emuno shelemo
> Bevias hamoshiach
> Bevias hamoshiach
> Ani ma-amin
> Veaf al pi
> Sheyismameach
> Im kol zeh
> Ani ma-amin
> Ani ma-amin
> Ani ma-amin ..."

They exit one at a time through the back door, repeating "Ani ma-amin" until they have all gone

Anne remains alone

Anne (*chanting, translating the gist of their final prayer*) "I believe that the Messiah will come. And even though he is a little late I will still believe." People of the World. Save us. Before it's too late. I'm trying to hear your voice, your protest. Children of the world, remember me. I was born. I lived for a while. I fell in love and then I went back again into the dark. (*She dances*) Life is the beautiful light in the entire darkness of time. I dance. Dance because I believe that I exist and I love and I will exist and love forever. Against all the odds. We are beautiful, and yes, we are loving. And we will love one another. One day. All of us. Everywhere. You'll see. Before I go down into the dark, into the night and fog, please remember me. And peace will come. And a thousand centuries of leaves and wind and rain and snow will cover the snow, again and again. And people will come and go. And fall in love. And peace will come. And peace will come. Goodbye, Diary.

Anne kisses her diary and reluctantly discards it, putting it down upon the pile of clothes heaped on the stage, and she exits through the back door, following the others

Her diary seems to light up the darkness that now envelops everything

SCENE D

Otto enters

Otto We were in that attic for two years. Until we were betrayed. And then we were taken on that terrible journey, to Auschwitz, where millions of us died, by gas. The war was almost over. Margot and Anne were moved to Germany. It was March, nineteen forty-five. Anne was fifteen. There, in Bergen-Belsen, Margot and Anne died from typhus. Desolate. Alone. A few weeks later the German army surrendered. It was that close. Irony. Anyway, it was all over. All our children went up together, into that exodus, into the clouds, leaving us behind, with dreams, memories, fragments of time. But sometimes I can hear their laughter upon the wind. Her book is special, yet what can replace the laughter of a living child? Anne's book is a marvel, because it contains and captures the hopes and the dreams and the fears of a girl who bore witness to the fact that we were here. That we were cut off and denied our lives, so cruelly. But words are inadequate. This book is precious, yet it is only a book and life is the most precious thing of all. All the books ever written cannot be weighed against the value of one child's life. I would gladly swap it, throw it away, or have it unwritten if I could only have Anne again, living. (*He closes the diary*)

Black-out

THE EVIL EYE OF GONDÔR
by Bryan Owen

A traveller comes to the Valley, which has been dominated by the Guardians of the Castle of Gondôr. For many, many years, their power has come from 'The Eye', and the cruelty of these Guardians, whose master is Roth, has broken the spirit of nearly all the villagers, and, except for a few outlaws, there is no hope. But the visiting Stranger helps them overcome their fears and conquer evil. These are the last four scenes of the drama. Consideration should be given to a simple setting and how best to use the acting space, with exciting visual and sound effects.

Set: the Market Square of Little Brumley, the Castle of Gondôr, near the Castle, the Castle of Gondôr. Period: a long time ago.

Cast: 10 main speaking parts (male or mixed). Extras.
Storyteller. Will, a village boy. Stout, his brother. The Mayor, friendly but fussy. The Stranger, a traveller. Kafka, a Guardian who is spying. Villagers, all poor. Roth, the Master of the Guardians, frightening and fearful, wears a dark half-mask. Jonah and Scamp, young outlaws. The Guardians. Rowan and Martin, prisoners. Mack, leader of the outlaws. Outlaws.

Playing time: 16 minutes.

Scene A

The Market Square of Little Brumley

The Villagers are "frozen" while the Storyteller speaks

Storyteller This is a fine how-do-you-do! The Stranger has put the cat among the pigeons now! Who'd have thought it? Only yesterday we were preparing for our harvest dance, as normal as you please, and today we're threatened with starvation, the Outlaws are in the Castle dungeons and the Stranger is calling for an uprising! (*He pauses*) Exciting, isn't it?

Everyone comes to life

Will Stranger, I don't quite understand you. Exactly how can we rid ourselves of the Guardians?

Stranger The first thing to do is to find the source of their power.

Mayor But we know that! It's the Eye.

Stranger That's what you've always believed, but that's where you're wrong.

Mayor Wrong? Wrong? Oh dear me, how can that be wrong?

Stranger Mr Mayor, it's not the Eye that's the source of their power—it's you!

Mayor Me? Me? I'm the source of their power? How dare you——

Stranger No, Mr Mayor. Don't misunderstand me. It's not you personally. It's everyone.

Will I still don't understand you, Stranger.

Stranger Now, think! You all believe in the power of the Eye. When the Guardians say they have power over you you all believe them. For generations you have taught your children to fear the Guardians and for generations you *have* feared the Guardians. And all the time you believe it the Guardians are safe.

Kafka, disguised as a Villager, enters and stands nearby

Stout Do you mean to say that we're being hoodwinked? That we've been hoodwinked all these years?

Stranger That's exactly what I mean. You are the slaves of your own fear, no more and no less.

Mayor Why, this is preposterous! Nonsense! I've never heard anything so ridiculous in all my life!

Stranger Mr Mayor. What could be more ridiculous than believing in an Eye that none of you has ever seen in a Castle that none of you has ever entered?

Mayor But the Guardians! What about them? We've seen them all right.

Stranger The strength of their power is in the strength of your fear.

Stout My dad didn't fear them and look what happened to him!

Stranger No, he didn't fear them when he was safe in the forest, but when he came face to face with them then his fear got the better of him! But there is a way of defeating them!

Will How's that, then Stranger?

All Yes, how? Tell us! *etc., etc.*

Stranger Listen! Listen! All of you! (*He pauses for silence*) The first battle you have to win is the battle with yourselves. You must take off your Eye badges.

There is consternation and cries of What? Never! etc.

If you are resolved not to fear the Eye and not to fear the Guardians then why wear their badge? It's a badge of fear. Tear it off. (*To Will*) How about it, Will? Will you be the first? Tear it off!

Will looks at his badge and he looks at the Stranger. He brings his hands up. His actions reflect his inner struggle

Will I can't! I can't! I've always worn this badge, ever since I was a child. It's part of me! I just can't do it!

Stranger Yes you can, Will. Your fear of the Eye is a fear of your own making. You chose to fear—now choose not to. If you win this battle you'll win all battles! Go on! Tear it off! Go on!

Will finally tears off his badge. The Villagers gasp, some with shock, some with surprise

Now how about you, Stout? Take off your badge. You don't belong to the Guardians anymore!

Stout goes through a similar process before pulling off his badge. Will cheers him and together they throw their badges on the ground. Then the Stranger, Will and Stout go through the crowd encouraging the others to do the same. They all do so, except the Mayor

Stranger Now, Mr Mayor. It's your turn. Will you tear off your badge?

Mayor Most certainly not. I've always worn my badge. It's the law. I can't give up my old ways just because a stranger suddenly comes and tells us to.

Will But Mr Mayor! You're the only one wearing a badge now. You're the odd one out.

Stout Come on, Mr Mayor. What have you got to lose?

Mayor My freedom, that's what I've got to lose. My freedom. Just wait till the Guardians hear about this!

Stranger You're wrong, Mr Mayor. Your freedom is what you have to gain. At the moment you're the only slave in the Village. It's the Guardians' turn to fear now.

The Mayor looks round. As he does so the Villagers encourage him with shouts of: Come on, Mr Mayor! You can do it! etc., etc. After a long inner struggle his hands begin to move towards his badge. The struggle continues until he finally tears it free. The Villagers cheer

Kafka makes an inconspicuous exit

Stranger Now! Listen! (*He waits for the cheering to die down*) If we work together you can have your dance tonight, and your harvest, and your families.

The Villagers all cheer

The first thing you need is weapons—anything you can lay your hands on—pitchforks, knives, hoes, brooms. Anything. Off you go! We meet back here in half an hour!

With much excitement the Villagers exit, except the Storyteller

Storyteller Exciting, isn't it? Now, what shall I take? I could use this broom, I suppose. What do you think? I can't wait to get started. There's something new happening in this Valley; there's a smell of change in the air. Still, I can't help wondering what the Guardians are going to make of all this ...

The Storyteller exits

The Lights fade to a Black-out

Scene B

Another part of the Castle

Roth and Kafka are talking

Roth Ah, Kafka. What's the news?
Kafka It's bad, my Lord.
Roth Well, tell me!
Kafka The Stranger has all the Villagers on his side. They're marching to the Castle.
Roth We've met that little problem before. We'll prepare our usual warm welcome!
Kafka That may not be so easy this time, my Lord. The people have removed their badges.
Roth What?!
Kafka The Stranger is very clever. He knows our weakness.
Roth He is clever indeed. So the people think they have lost their fear, do they? Wait until they approach the Castle—we'll see if we can't remind them what real fear is. Come, Kafka! I have a little plan!

Roth and Kafka exit

The Lights fade to a Black-out

Scene C

Near the Castle

The Villagers, all carrying weapons of some sort, enter, led by the Stranger

Stranger Keep together. Don't straggle.

Mayor How much further? My old legs won't carry me.
Will Don't worry, Mr Mayor. Just you wait until we meet the Guardians. You'll be
all right then.
Mayor Meeting the Guardians is just what I'm worrying about.

*There is a clap of thunder and a burst of lightning. It continues. Action goes to slow
motion to emphasize the length of the journey*

Stranger Don't be afraid. Stay together.

*The journey to the Castle takes the form of a slow motion circle on the stage. The
thunder fades to be replaced by sundry eerie noises: maniacal laughter, a whistling
wind, animal's roar, etc.*

(*Standing erect and waving the Villagers on*) Don't listen! They're only tricks to
frighten you!
Stout They're succeeding! Ohhh!

Eventually all the noises fade to silence

Roth and Kafka appear at the edge of the stage, unseen by the Villagers

Roth It's not working! They should be terrified by now!
Kafka I told you the Stranger was clever.
Roth I'll show him who's clever!

Roth and Kafka exit

The journey continues

Stranger Not far to go now. We're almost there!

Further eerie sounds are heard

Monsters and Spirits enter to haunt the Villagers

Don't look at them! They don't exist! They are only figments of your imaginations!
Keep your heads down. Don't look at them! (*He repeats himself as long as is
necessary to calm the Villagers*)

The Monsters and Spirits exit and the sounds die away

Roth and Kafka appear as before

Roth And still they come!

Kafka What next, my Lord?
Roth We wait—until they reach the Castle. We'll see how brave they are when they
meet—the Guardians!

Roth and Kafka exit

The journey continues

Jonah This is it! This is where Mack and the others were captured.
Scamp I'm scared.

The Villagers look round. They are scared too

Stranger Now listen everybody. Whatever happens, do exactly as I say. Don't go
off by yourself—stay close. And whatever you see, remember—they're counting
on your fear to win the battle.

*As before there is a throbbing sound, menacing and oppressive. The Villagers are
startled. The Lights begin to throb with the sound*

The Guardians appear out of the shadows

*The Guardians raise their arms and point to the Villagers who clap their hands over
their ears and slowly begin to collapse in great pain*

Roth appears

Roth I am Roth! Who dares approach the Castle of Gondôr?
Stranger Don't look at the Guardians! Don't listen!

*The Stranger rushes round the company, encouraging them when they falter. Some
look at the ground, some are tempted to look at the Guardians*

Guardians (*chanting*) Look at us! Look at us! Look at us! Gondôr! Gondôr! Gondôr!
(*and so on*)
Stranger Don't look! Don't look! Look at the ground!

*The battle goes on, and as the struggle for the Villagers continues, more and more
people look at the ground and become perfectly still*

As this happens the Guardians slowly withdraw

The throbbing sound dies away until there is silence and stillness

Roth exits

Will We've won! We've won!

All the Villagers cheer and shout

Stranger Listen to me! (*He waits for quiet*) We haven't won yet. We are still outside the Castle. The Guardians are almost defeated, but they are not destroyed. We must find a way into the Castle.
Jonah If I remember rightly, the door is around that corner. (*He points off*)
Stranger That's the way in then. Come on everyone!

Everyone exits

The Lights fade to Black-out

SCENE D

The Castle of Gondôr

The Outlaws are chained

Roth, Brasov and Kafka enter

Roth (*to Kafka*) We are not finished yet! There is still the Eye!
Kafka But what good will that do? I'm the one who fears now!
Roth Fear? What does a Guardian know of fear? (*Pointing to the Outlaws*) It is they who must fear!
Rowan We don't fear you, Roth! You're finished! Why don't you give up now?

Brasov hits Rowan who collapses, dazed

Roth Stop snivelling, Kafka!
Kafka But the Stranger has entered the Castle! He'll be here any minute!
Roth Let him come. Let them all come! I don't care! The Eye will teach them!
Kafka But the Eye has no power, you know that! The Stranger is right—we rely on the people's own fear. We always have. And now they have no fear—but I do!

The Villagers enter, cheering, with some Guardians who are fighting a rearguard action

The Guardians are driven back and go to stand with Roth, Brasov and Kafka behind the Eye

Stranger Roth! The game is up! We demand your surrender!
Roth Surrender? Who are you to make demands, Stranger? It is I, Roth, who demands your surrender. People of the Valley—lay down your arms!

The people falter and look to the Stranger

Stranger They no longer fear you, Roth. You no longer have power over this Valley.
Roth No longer have power? People don't change, Stranger. They still fear, deep
   down inside—you can't change that. Watch!

*Roth points to the Eye which begins to glow. The Guardians raise their arms and
point to the Eye. As its light throbs so it is accompanied by dreadful sounds. It grows
dark in the Castle, except for the light of the Eye. The Villagers react with horror*

Stranger It's a trick! Look away! Look away!

*The Stranger runs around making the Villagers look away from the Eye. They clap
their hands over their ears and grit their teeth, feeling the pain but not giving in to it.
The Stranger then forces his way among the Guardians until he finds a "cable"
behind the Eye. He cuts it; there is an explosion, a flash and the Eye's light goes out.
The noises fade. The Castle lights come up*

All right, you can look now! See ... it's a fake. That is your "Eye"!

*The Guardians try to escape. They are caught. The Outlaws are freed from their
chains and the Guardians chained in their place*

Mack Well ... it's all over, then?
Stranger All over. The Guardians only maintained their power because deep down
   inside you wanted them to. When you began to resist it was inevitable that their
   power should crumble away. Now that you know the truth about the so-called
   "Eye" you can be free from its influence.
Mack (*pointing to the Guardians*) What are we going to do about them?
Stranger That will be up to you. For now, I'd suggest you offer them the same
   hospitality they offered you. With them out of the way you can all go back to Little
   Brumley and enjoy that harvest dance, can't you?
Mayor That we can, Stranger. That we can!
Roth We nearly won, you know, Stranger.
Stranger Yes, Roth. You nearly did.
Roth Do you think the people have lost their fear? When it came to the crunch they
   needed you, didn't they?
Stranger But they won, Roth. In the end they won. You can never take that away.
Roth And if a new fear replaces the old?
Stranger Then they'll know what to do, won't they? (*To the Villagers*) Tomorrow
   you've got decisions to make, but today? Today is harvest! Today we dance!

*The Villagers cheer then the action is frozen as the Storyteller slowly makes his way
through the tableau*

Storyteller So there we are: the end of the story. Tonight we dance after all. Young Will will be chasing Mistress Marion; Stout will have eyes on Mistress Lucy. Tomorrow Rowan and Martin will go back to Upper Lonsdale and watch the sheep on the high pasture. The Outlaws can go home again and sit by their firesides. And me? Well, I rather fancy Mistress Rachel ... aaah! A lot has happened when you think of it, ever since the Stranger arrived. We never did find out who he really was, at least not until a long while after ... when we read it in the Ancient Writings. But this is where our story ends. Good-night!

GRINLING GIBBONS AND THE PLAGUE OF LONDON
by Brian Way

The play is set in London at the time of the plague. In this scene, the talented wood-carver, Grinling Gibbons protects a young musician, Silvio Doria, from the mob. The setting of street and shop could be on different levels, and the cast is flexible, as there could be double casting of street characters.

Set: The scene is a London street and an old curiosity shop, moving back into the street and finally into Grinling Gibbons's house. Period: 1665.

Cast: M6 F2.
1st Death-cart Man. 2nd Death-cart Man. A Man. A Woman. Grinling Gibbons, the wood-carver. Mistress Leah Benoni. Simeon Benoni, her father, the mean owner of the old curiosity shop. Silvio Doria, an Italian boy, a musical entertainer.

Playing time: 12 minutes.

Plague-stricken London of 1665. There is the distant ringing of a handbell

Voice (*off, distant*) Bring out the dead.

Distant footsteps

(*Off, distant*) Bring out the dead.

Distant cart noise

(*Off, nearer*) Bring out the dead.

The sounds draw near. They stop

A body is carried to the cart by two death-cart men. A man and a woman stand near

1st Death-cart Man May God have mercy on his soul.

Man　⎱ (*together*) Amen.
Woman　⎰

They hold each other tightly in a grip of lonely despair

The death-cart men go

The footsteps, the voice, the bell, the cart-wheels all fade away. As they go, the woman cries quietly, nearly all grief spent. And as she cries, she and the man walk together down the street; their only comfort is in the nearness of each other. But the bitter desperation in their hearts can be heard in their footsteps

As they go, a young man — Grinling Gibbons — enters and walks to the end of the street and into an old curiosity shop. There is a counter behind which works Mistress Leah. The bell rings as Grinling enters. He carries a carved box (wrapped). He stands watching and listening

Leah Seventeen, eighteen, nineteen, twenty. So much for the Earl of Rochester. Now — Lord Sandwich — gold work to order fifteen pounds. And Sir A. Paulett, for curiously inlaid cabinet, owing ten pounds.
Gibbons Good-day, Mistress Leah.
Leah Your pardon, Master Gibbons. Did you wish to see my father?
Gibbons If it please you, Mistress Leah, I have brought the box.
Leah Oh! Let me see it, Master Gibbons.

He unwraps it

Oh, it's lovely, Master Gibbons. Beautiful. It must be worth more than anything in the shop. His lordship cannot fail to be pleased with such beautiful work.

Simeon Benoni enters

Simeon (*as he enters*) Eh? What is it? What is it, daughter? What is so beautiful?
Leah Master Gibbons has brought the box, Father.
Simeon Good-day, Master Gibbons. Hmm. Hmm. Yes, yes, very fair, very fair. Yes, it does you marvellous credit, Master Gibbons. If you go on as you've begun — well, who can tell? — you may become a great carver one day. Just take heed to be true to nature — a little more exactness, eh, my lad?
Gibbons Thank you for your good opinion of me, Master Simeon. Now — er ...
Simeon Yes, yes. What is it?
Gibbons Well, about the price ... ?
Simeon Ah, yes, the price. Hmm. The price. Well, I've hardly considered it yet. Suppose you come back in a day or two.
Gibbons But sir, my need is immediate. I — I must live.

Simeon Very true, my lad, very true. Then you shall have it at once. What say you to a pound?

Gibbons Master Simeon, I could not sell my work for that. Remember the material, the time, the labour.

Simeon Well, well, I don't want to drive a close bargain. I'm no hard man. Say one pound five. No? You are not easily satisfied, are you? One pound ten?

Gibbons Master Simeon, I've said I must live. I don't like haggling, so I'll tell you my lowest price. Two pounds, ten shillings, Master Simeon. I can take nothing less.

Simeon Heard you ever such a thing? Two pound ten, say you? You must have a mighty good opinion of your work, Master Gibbons. 'Tis by no means perfect, I can tell you. Tcha, you ungrateful boy. You should remember the encouragement I've given you — I alone — before you ask such exorbitant prices.

Gibbons My price is not exorbitant, sir. 'Tis a bare return for my labour. And I know you will receive far more from Lord Waterdale for it.

Simeon No, no, I shall lose by it. I shall lose. Come now, Master Gibbons. Two pounds would repay you. Come, say two pounds.

Gibbons Two pounds ten shillings, Master Simeon.

Simeon Ah, well — so be it. But I shall lose by it, I tell you. Hand me the money, child.

Leah (*whispering to Simeon*) Father, it's worth more. You know his Lordship offered five pounds —

Simeon Hush child, hush. Here, my lad. Take your money.

Gibbons Thank you, Master Simeon. And have you — have you any other commissions for me?

Simeon Well, I — I *have* had an order of the kind this very day — but I doubt whether you can do it.

Gibbons I can try, sir. What is it?

Simeon 'Tis but a lady's whim, my lad, a mere whim. It seems my Lady Springfield has laid a bet with my Lady Betty Gray that a pot of flowers can be carved in wood so cunningly as scarce to be known from nature. I told her I thought it hardly possible, for how are the delicate stalks and leaves to stand upright without a wooden background to support them? No, I hardly think you would succeed with that commission.

Gibbons When must the work be done?

Simeon It must be in my hands by a month today.

Mob noise starts off. A pursuit. Voices: "To the river, to the river", "Down with Papists", intermingled with cries for "mercy", "pity". It grows gradually

Gibbons Thank you, Master Simeon. I will do my best.

Simeon You will need the finest tools, my lad.

Gibbons This (*holding up money*) will buy them.

Simeon What is that noise, child?

They listen. Leah goes to the window

Leah 'Tis an Italian boy being chased by the mob. They're coming this way.

Gibbons runs to the door as the noise increases. The "pity" cry draws nearer

    Silvio Doria, well ahead of the mob, reaches the shop

Gibbons pulls him into the shop and holds him back against the wall

Gibbons Be still.

They stand breathlessly waiting

    The crowd arrives

The leader, Foster, comes into the shop. Gibbons pushes Silvio farther back

Foster Did a swarthy Italian boy pass this way, Mistress Leah?
Leah Yes, Master Foster, he ran past the shop.
Foster Thank you, Mistress. We'll catch him — the papist poisoner.

    He runs on, followed by the mob

Gibbons Your pardon, Master Simeon. Quickly, my friend, this way.

    He runs out of the shop, followed by Silvio

Leah and Simeon are alone

Leah Why do they chase a mere boy like that?
Simeon Who knows? He was a foreigner.
Leah What of that?
Simeon They poison the waters and bring the plague upon us. Master Foster is one who has suffered.
Leah Suffered?
Simeon Yes, my child, so I am told.
Leah From the plague?
Simeon It took away one of his children only last week. The other is sick also.
Leah God have mercy on them.
Simeon Amen to that. My child — we know nothing of this incident.
Leah No, Father. But they will be safely home by now ——
Simeon Tush, tush, child. Go inside at once.

They go into another room. As they disappear, Gibbons and Silvio arrive at the end of their journey — Gibbons' house

Gibbons Still! Listen! Phooh. There's no-one following. You're safe here.
Silvio Thank you, signor.

They go into the house

Gibbons Sit over here and get your breath back.
Silvio Thank you, thank you signor.
Gibbons Nonsense, man. You'd have done the same for me. What's your name?
Silvio Silvio Doria.
Gibbons Mine's Grinling Gibbons. Italian?
Silvio Si, signor.
Gibbons Are you musical? You Italians usually are.
Silvio Si, signor. Oh, but signor, I had forgotten them.
Gibbons Who?
Silvio Filippo and my violin. My only friends. I have lost them, signor.
Gibbons Come, now, pull yourself together. We can find them again when the mob's dispersed. Where did you lose them?
Silvio Oh, signor, you do not understand. You are good — but those people — oh they are cruel. They have killed Filippo.
Gibbons Killed him? Who is Filippo?
Silvio My bambino — my, how do you say — monkey?
Gibbons I'm sorry, Silvio. How did it happen?
Silvio I play my violin. Filippo, he sits on my shoulder. People they come and listen to my music. Some throw money into the hat at my feet. Then, when the crowd is big, Filippo dances the tarantella — oh, signor my Filippo danced so beautiful. Then suddenly he sees a little boy trying to steal pennies from the hat — and he tries to stop him.
Gibbons Did he hurt the little boy?
Silvio No, signor. As soon as he touched him, the mama of the boy picks up Filippo and throws him. She killed him, signor —
Gibbons And then —
Silvio She turned on me. She called me outlandish Papist and vermin and said it was me and my kind that started the plague. And all the crowd yelled at me. One big man, he grabs my vest and tears off my crucifix and they all stamp on it and shout louder and louder and attack me. They would have killed me but for you, signor. Why they do it signor, why they do it?
Gibbons They do it because you are a Roman Catholic, Silvio. 'Tis the enemies of the Duke of York who whisper all these wicked stories of the Papists poisoning the waters and so on, to set folk against him. Personally, I don't see why a man should be branded a traitor, spy, poisoner, and so on just because he's a Roman Catholic. Not that I'm one myself, but I don't like injustice. What is it, Silvio?

Silvio My violin. He is dead.

Gibbons Did they break it?

Silvio They crushed it under their feet, signor. They crushed it to splinters. Oh, signor.

Gibbons Don't be upset, Silvio. That won't mend the fiddle.

Silvio You say that because you not know. My violin was my all — my food, my joy, my friend. My father, he gave it me, my dear father who is dead. All are dead — my mother, Giovannetto, little Maria, Filippo — all are dead. And now, too, my violin.

Gibbons Silvio, you mustn't worry anymore. Look here. See — this will buy you another fiddle.

Silvio Signor, I cannot take your gold.

Gibbons Why not?

Silvio You will want it. The signor does not look rich.

Gibbons Never mind that. I would like to buy you one. Then you can play for me. Here, please take it.

Silvio Signor, I cannot thank you. I know not enough your English words. Oh, bless you, signor.

Gibbons There, there, you've thanked me enough.

Silvio You are poor, and yet you give me money to buy the violin. May the dear Lord reward you, signor. You are the only one who has been kind to me since I left my own country.

Gibbons You go and buy your violin, Silvio. Then you can come back tomorrow to play for me while I work on my new commission.

Silvio Will it be safe now do you think, signor?

Gibbons Quite safe. They'll have forgotten all about you by now.

Silvio Grazie, signor, grazie.

He goes

HANS, THE WITCH AND THE GOBBIN
by Alan Cullen

Hans, a medical student, is helping Princess Alicia recover her memory, which has been stolen by the zany witch, Daisy, a collector of memories. In this humorous scene, Daisy has fun tricking the King, Scratch, his secretary, Mrs Crabtree, a dowser, and the physicians, Castor and Senna. Sylvester, the swineherd, with his pigs Hank and Hunk, become involved in offering to help the Princess and Hans.

Set: The Forest.

Cast: M6 F3, 2 M or F. 1 female voice.
Daisy Crowfoot, a witch, a fantastic figure, crazily restless, whose every movement and tone of voice expresses utter eccentricity. She cannot be too odd. Mrs Crabtree, a dowser, an intense character in tweed dress and cape. King Rufus. Princess Alicia, his daughter, whose memory has been stolen by Daisy. Hans, a young medical student of pleasing appearance. Scratch, secretary to the king. Sylvester, an exquisitely dressed swineherd. Hank and Hunk, two pigs with lace collars and blue bows on their tails. Castor and Senna, physicians. Queen of the Forest's voice.

Playing time: 30 minutes.

The Forest

There is a tree ULC, *a log for a seat* DC *and a small length of fencing* DL

The stage is empty. After a moment, Daisy, in great excitement, enters hurriedly UR

Daisy (*circling the stage*) Oops, Daisy! Daisy's on the run. One, two, three, they can't catch me. Oh, such a run for their money. Whoops and tiddy-fol-lol, girls, let me get me breath for a minute. (*She sits on the log* C *and vigorously fans herself with a corner of her shawl*) Oh, dear—oh, dear—oh, dear! "Age cannot wither her", as the poet says, but, my word, he's doing his best. Daisy ain't as young as she was.

Mrs Crabtree (*off; calling*) Rally! Rally! Rally! Rally! Follow me. Crabtree never fails.
Daisy (*rising*) Harden me arteries. They're after me yet. Heel and toe, here we go; oh, my witchdom for a broomstick. "Fly farther off", as the poet says, "there is no tarradiddle here". A bane on Mrs Crabtree. (*She is capering off, but stops suddenly*) Wait! No! That isn't the way, Daisy. Crabtree must be foiled. Crabtree is formidable, but Daisy is formidabbler. Whoops! They shall not pass. (*She dives a hand into her capacious pocket and produces a red herring*) "A little red herring said to me, 'boot and saddle and off to sea.'"
Mrs Crabtree (*off*) Rally! Rally!
Daisy Rally, rally, I reply. (*She trails the herring round in a circle on the ground, then nips behind the tree to watch*) Neat and tidy, fish on Friday. Oh, Daisy's artful.
Mrs Crabtree (*off*) Follow the hazel twig.

Mrs Crabtree enters UR, *hot and flustered, the hazel twig rampant*

(*As she enters and comes* DC) We're getting warmer, Euripides. Follow the dowsing rod.

The King enters UR. *Scratch, puffing and blowing, follows the King on*

King (*moving* DRC) Stop!

Mrs Crabtree stops

Mrs Crabtree, I cannot and will not go another step farther. This confounded mumbo-jumbo of yours is getting us nowhere.
Mrs Crabtree Oh, but it is. It is. Look at the rod. I can hardly hold it. We're almost there, I'm sure of it.
King Oh, very well. I'm almost past feeling, anyway.

Mrs Crabtree continues. The twig pulls her to one side of the stage, then jerks uncertainly from side to side

Mrs Crabtree There's—there's something wrong. A cross-influence is confusing the rod. Oh!

The last cry is rather desperate, as the twig drags her smartly off again, to follow the circle Daisy made with the herring. Mrs Crabtree tears round, the King and Scratch dully following. Finally she spirals round into C *and stops. As she looks in dismay at the twig, it snaps in two with a loud crack*

(*Horrified*) Oh!
King Crabtree always gets her witch, eh?

The King and Scratch sit on the log

Mrs Crabtree (*moving* LC) This is most frustrating. I've never been so close to the kill, and then for this to happen. What *will* your Majesty think of me?
Scratch (*his idol shattered*) Oh, Auntie!
Mrs Crabtree I don't understand it. Just when the trail was so fresh, and this was my very best dowsing-rod, too.
King (*rising*) Well, I suppose all we can do now is to return to the palace. Come, Scratch.

Scratch rises

Scratch (*with a reproachful look at Mrs Crabtree*) Yes, your Majesty.

Mrs Crabtree hangs her head. The King moves UC, *then looks uncertainly about him*

King Er—Scratch.
Scratch Sir?
King (*pointing* R *and* L) Did we come that way or that way?
Scratch I don't know. (*He points* DL) This way, wasn't it?
King Don't ask me, I'm asking *you*.
Scratch And I'm telling you I don't know.
King Don't use that tone with me, Scratch.
Scratch I wasn't using a tone.
King Yes, you were.
Scratch No, I wasn't.
King I said you were.
Scratch Oh, all right, I'm sorry.
King That's better.
Scratch You always blame things on me.
King (*moving* DC) That will do. And don't let's quarrel, whatever we do.

Mrs Crabtree moves L *of the King, Scratch to* R *of him*

If, as I strongly suspect, we are lost in this forest ...
Scratch Lost?
King I'm afraid so. And, as I say, *if* we are, the only way we shall get ourselves out of it is by being nice and friendly with each other, and not snapping each other's heads off. Mrs Crabtree.
Mrs Crabtree (*humbly*) Yes?
King Do *you* know where we are?
Mrs Crabtree I'm afraid I don't. I just follow the scent regardless. I have little sense of direction, I fear.
King Just as I thought. Then we *are* lost.

There is a short silence, then Scratch kneels and begins to sniff as though he were going to cry

(*He looks at Scratch*) Scratch?
Scratch (*miserably*) Yes?
King Are you crying?
Scratch (*with a sniff*) No.
King You are.
Scratch I'm not.
King Yes, you are. And you mustn't. *I'm* not crying.

Scratch sniffs

Your Aunt Thingummy isn't crying.

Scratch sniffs

And so *you* mustn't cry.
Scratch (*with a wail*) But we're lost!
King (*moving a little* UC) Now, that's quite enough. I can't imagine what you're crying *for*. It isn't as if you were alone. I'm with you—your Aunt Thingummy's with you—so what on earth is there to be afraid of? Do you expect something to jump out of the forest and bite you or something?

Rumbling noises are heard off. Mrs Crabtree moves to L *of the King*

Scratch Yes.
King Well, it won't. If anyone is to be bitten it will be Mrs Crabtree. Now, just try to take your mind off it, and think of other things—nice things.
Scratch I—I'll try.
King Thank Heaven for that!
Scratch (*rising and moving* R *of the King*) Will you—(*he sniffs*) will you tell me a story?
King I certainly will not tell you a story.
Scratch I should feel much better if you would.

The King sees Scratch's lugubrious face looking at him

King Oh, all right, I—I'll see if I can remember something.
Scratch Thank you.

The King sits on the log. Scratch sits R *of him, Mrs Crabtree sits* L *of him. There is a pause while the King thinks. Daisy, unseen by the others, tiptoes from behind the tree and creeps behind the trio on the log. She is armed with a butterfly net*

King Are you sitting comfortably?
Scratch Yes.
King Then I will begin.
Daisy (*in a nervous whisper*) Gently does it, Daisy dear. Whoops, careful!
King Once upon a time ...

Daisy makes three snatches with the net in the air behind their heads. Their expressions go blank at once

Daisy (*as she snatches*) Snip, snap, snip! Three at a go. Daisy, you're a caution! (*She capers* RC, *takes three invisible handfuls out of the net, and pops them into her pocket*) Oh, lovely, lovely, lovely. Three beautiful memories to add to Daisy's priceless collection. (*She capers down* R) With a fal lal la and a derry down day. Oh, my Aunt Eliza. Royal reminiscences, secretarial secrets, and the daring doings of a dowser. Oh, sensational scavenging. Unprecedented pickings. What a time Daisy will have with herself, rummaging through this little heap of souvenirs. Ah, but wait! What? (*She moves behind the others*) Yes, what shall we do with the bodies? Turn them adrift, of course. Set them at liberty. "Liberty, Freedom—tyranny is dead", said the Bard, and who shall say him nay. Not Daisy, not on your life. (*She moves* C) Come, Euripides. (*She takes Scratch by the hand*)

Scratch rises and looking blankly at Daisy

Scratch Who are you?
Daisy What's more to the point is who are *you*?
Scratch Me? I think ... I don't know who I am.
Daisy Then why worry about me, little man? What can you recollect about yourself? H'm?
Scratch (*after a pause*) Nothing. (*He pauses*) I can remember nothing.
Daisy That's it! Not nothing, not nobody, nohow. Oh, clever Daisy. Then you'd better start looking for yourself, hadn't you? (*She turns him round*) Off you go, Euripides. (*She gives him a push*)

Scratch sets off vaguely into the forest and exits DL

(*Crossing to* L *of Mrs Crabtree*) You there!
Mrs Crabtree Do you mean me?
Daisy Yes, you. What are you doing here?
Mrs Crabtree What business is that of yours?
Daisy (*moving down* L) Oh, la la! Crabtree sauce, forsooth. (*She returns and sits* L *of Mrs Crabtree on the log*)
Mrs Crabtree If you must know, I'm—well, I'm—sitting in the forest with—(*she looks at the King*) a perfect stranger.

Daisy Well, don't you think you'd better stop it?
Mrs Crabtree (*rising*) Yes, I—I suppose I better had. (*She looks about her, bewildered*) Strange, I can't for the life of me remember how I came to be here, or who I am, or even what my name is.

Mrs Crabtree wanders UR *and exits*

Daisy moves along the log, sits beside the King and rests her head on his shoulder

King (*coming to his senses somewhat*) My good woman!
Daisy (*sitting up*) Oh, my elastic stockings! Daisy's never been called "good" before. Yes, my good man?
King I'm a little confused as to where I am. Can you possibly help me to find my way back to—to ... Bless my soul, I don't even know where I'm going.
Daisy Nor where you've been?
King Nor where I've been.
Daisy Nor who you are nor where you are nor what you are nor whether it's half-past six or Pancake Thursday? Eh? Do you? Is it?
King Yes. No. *Please*, please, I'm so confused, I—I can't think ...
Daisy (*rising and moving to* L *of the log*) Then don't.

The King rises and moves to R *of the log*

Thinking never did anybody any good, you know. I never think.

They bow to each other

I just act according to impulse. (*She moves to the King, grabs him and dances around with him*) And what impulses Daisy does get.

Daisy releases the King, crosses and exits DL

The King is left utterly bewildered

King (*crossing to* L) Oh, no—please come back just for a moment. I—I—I ... (*He turns uncertainly and goes* UL)

The Princess enters DL

The King turns and crosses to RC

(*Seeing the Princess; politely*) Good-afternoon. (*He moves* R, *stops, and turns, puzzled, to look at the Princess*)

The Princess looks at the King, puzzled, and shakes her head

  The King shakes his head and exits DR

The Princess starts to follow the King, then hesitates and moves UC

Princess If only I could remember—if only I could ...

  Hans enters DL

Hans Princess! (*He runs to her*) Are you all right? Thank goodness I've found you.
Princess Yes, I think so. I seem to know you. I've seen you somewhere before.
Hans Of course you have. In the palace.
Princess Yes. You are a doctor.
Hans In a way, I am. Tell me, why did you run away?
Princess Run away? Did I?
Hans Yes, don't you remember? We were all talking and you just got up and went out. Why?
Princess (*moving* DC) I think—I think I wanted to find someone.
Hans And did you?
Princess Not yet.
Hans Well, don't try to think anymore. (*He leads the Princess to the log*) Just rest, and presently we'll go back to your father.
Princess (*sitting on the log*) What is your name?
Hans Hans.
Princess Hans. You seem to understand me. I only wish I could understand myself. If only I could remember things ...
Hans Now, don't worry. (*He sits* L *of the Princess on the log*) Everything will turn out all right, you'll see.
Princess Of course. We don't have to go back *just* yet, do we?
Hans Not if you don't want to.
Princess It's nice in the forest. As I was walking through it just now, I—it was like discovering it for the first time. I suppose I've seen it before, but not remembering it, it all seems so fresh and new—how the sunlight makes moving patterns on the ground, and how if you stand quite still and don't breathe there's a kind of silence you don't find anywhere else—a silence you can almost hear. And then suddenly from nowhere at all there's a squirrel sitting right in front of you, licking its whiskers and paying no attention to you at all. You see, I can remember some things—recent things.
Hans Of course you can. It will all come back to you presently.
Princess (*rising*) I hope so. (*She moves* DR *and turns*) Hans.
Hans Yes, Princess?
Princess If I don't ever get my memory back ...

Hans (*rising*) You mustn't say things like that.

Princess No, but if I don't ...

Hans Well?

Princess Well, I don't think I should mind quite so much as long as I had someone—someone like you—with me.

Hans (*moving to the Princess and taking her hands*) I can think of nothing better than to be with you all the time, but ...

Princess But what?

Hans Well, you see, you are a princess, a king's daughter, very grand and important, and I—I'm nobody at all.

Princess I don't feel grand and important and you're—(*she crosses to* c *and turns to him*) you're Hans and you're very important to me. Promise you'll stay with me, Hans.

Hans I'll stay with you.

Princess (*sitting on the log*) I think I'm happy now—happier than I've been for a long time.

Hans Perhaps we ought to be starting back, now. (*He moves to the Princess*) The forest is large, and I'm not altogether sure of the way.

Princess Supposing we couldn't find our way out; then we should always be together, shouldn't we? That would be wonderful, to make the forest our home, and never go back to where it matters about being somebody or nobody.

Sylvester enters nonchalantly UL. *He is exquisitely, even ostentatiously dressed and looks quite out of place in such rural surroundings. One elegant hand is lightly holding the ends of two pink ribbons, the other ends of which are out of sight in the wings. For all that, he is only a swineherd*

Here, it doesn't matter at all who you are.

Sylvester Ah, but it does. (*He stands by the tree* ULC)

Hans and the Princess, startled, rise and turn to Sylvester

Hans Where did you spring from? (*He moves* R *of the log*)

The Princess moves DR *of Hans*

Sylvester Spring is hardly the word. I never do anything so vigorous if I can help it. You say it doesn't matter in the forest who you are; let me inform you it matters a great deal. Take me, for instance. I am quite definitely Somebody in these parts.

Hans Would it be very much out of place to ask who you are?

Sylvester Not at all. I can see you are a stranger in the forest. My name is Sylvester.

Hans How do you do? My name is Hans. I am a student.

Sylvester Of what?

Hans Medicine. And this is my patient, the Princess.

Sylvester Princess who?

Hans *The* Princess. The King's daughter.

Sylvester (*moving* DL *of the log*) Ah. (*To the Princess*) How do you do.

Princess How do you do.

Sylvester What king?

Hans King Rufus, of course.

Sylvester Why "of course"? *I* never heard of him.

Hans But you must be one of his subjects.

Sylvester Not in the least. I owe allegiance only to the Queen of the Forest, whom I
serve.

Hans Well, *I* never heard of her, so that makes us even.

Sylvester (*sitting on the log*) Even, perhaps; equal, never.

Hans Look, what *are* you, really?

Sylvester What am I? I am Swineherd to the Queen.

Hans A swineherd? Is *that* all?

Sylvester *All?* It is a very great deal, I assure you. There are swine and swine, you
know. Swineherd to the Queen is an office of some moment.

Hans Where are your swine, then?

Sylvester On the other end of these ribbons. Would you care to meet them?

Hans I can hardly wait.

Sylvester hauls on the ribbons

Hank and Hunk trot on L, *cross and stand one each side of the Princess. They have
lace collars and blue bows on their tails*

Sylvester Allow me to introduce Hank and Hunk, the Queen's Swine. (*To Hank and
Hunk*) Say, "How do you do" to the lady and gentleman.

Hank (*bobbing to the Princess*) Hoink!

Hunk (*bobbing to the Princess*) Hoink, hoink!

Princess How do you do. They really are rather sweet.

Sylvester They are highly accomplished animals, ma'am, and terribly well bred.

Princess But won't their collars get dirty, grubbing about in the forest?

Hank and Hunk look horrified and retreat DR

Sylvester Grubbing about? They never do that.

Hank (*deprecatingly*) Hoink!

Hunk (*loftily*) Hoink, hoink, hoink!

Hank and Hunk cross above the others to L *of Sylvester*

Sylvester Hunk is the talkative one. No, you see, they don't feed in the forest. But they like to take a little stroll now and then, when the weather is fine. If it isn't, they continue their lessons.

Princess Lessons? Pigs taking lessons?

Sylvester And why not?

Princess But what do they learn?

Sylvester (*rising and crossing to* L) Oh, dancing, fencing, watercolours; you know the sort of thing. Their gavotte is quite something.

Hank and Hunk display well-bred excitement at the mention of the gavotte, hoinking and clapping their trotters

There! I shouldn't have mentioned it. They won't be satisfied now until they've given you a demonstration. Stop it, you little pigs.

Hank and Hunk subside

(*To the Princess*) Do you mind very much? They do like to show off, I'm afraid.

Princess (*sitting on the log*) Oh, do let them.

Sylvester I'll just loosen their collars first. (*He removes the ribbons*)

Hank and Hunk take their places for the gavotte

(*Beating time and counting*) And——

Music is heard. Hank and Hunk dance

—one and two and three and point; one and two and three and point; one and two and ...

Sylvester, during the dance, crosses above the log to L of Hans. Hank and Hunk, when they have finished their dance, bow to each other, then jump up and down, clapping their trotters and hoinking

No, you mustn't go through it again.

Hank and Hunk move to Sylvester and hoink the more

No, I said, and that's final.

Hank and Hunk turn their backs

(*To Hans*) It doesn't do to give way to them too much.

Princess They are very clever, but why do they get such special treatment? After all, they are only pigs.

Sylvester (*sitting* R *of the Princess on the log*) Now, that's where you are mistaken, ma'am. They are very special pigs, in fact, magic pigs. You don't imagine the Queen of the Forest would have anything ordinary, do you?

Hans (*crossing to Hank and Hunk*) *Magic* pigs, eh? *We* could do with a little magic just now.

Hank ⎫
Hunk ⎬ (*together*) Hoink!

Sylvester Really? But why ever didn't you say? (*He strikes a pose*) I'm magic, too, you know—a sort of Fairy Swineherd you might call me. (*He turns to the Princess*) It's a very enchanted locality, taking it all round. What exactly is the trouble?

Hans Well, it's the Princess, mainly. Her memory has been stolen—she's bewitched.

Sylvester No!

Hans Yes, indeed.

Sylvester Well, I never! You know who has it, of course?

Hans That's it, you see, we don't. (*He moves above the log*)

Sylvester (*leaning down to the Princess*) Oh, that makes it *very* awkward.

Princess But we do—at least, I do.

Hans But you never told anybody you knew who it was.

Princess Perhaps nobody thought of asking me.

Hans Who is it, then?

Princess It's somebody called Daisy.

Hans Daisy?

Princess Yes, I can't recall her other name.

Hank and Hunk jump about and hoink

Sylvester Just a minute. I think they know.

Hank and Hunk move to Sylvester and clamour for attention, with much hoinking and pointing

Oh, please, please. Don't both hoink at once. One at a time, now.

Hank and Hunk subside a little, and an elaborate conversation ensues as they hoink alternately, interspersed with Sylvester's comments

Yes ... Yes ... Over there ... I see ... *Is* she? ... *Does* she? ... She *didn't!* ... What? ... Yes ... All right, I've got it ... I've got it. (*He rises and pushes them* DR) All *right*, I said. (*To the Princess*) Really there's no stopping them once they start.

Princess What did they say?

Sylvester Well, it seems that over the other side of the forest lives a witch called— Daisy Crockett or Crewcut or something ...

Hunk *Hoink-hoink!*

Sylvester What? "Crowfoot", that's it—Crowfoot. Well now, she is the one, and from what they say she is *the* most powerful witch ever. And believe me, they know.

Hank Hoink!

The Princess rises and moves DLC. *Hans moves to the Princess*

Sylvester It appears she steals people's memories and keeps them in little glass bottles, all neatly labelled like medicine.

Princess But what for?

Sylvester Now, how can you expect pigs to know that?

Hank } *(together)* Hoink!
Hunk }

Hans Did they tell you any more?

Sylvester Oh, lots. They could write a book about Daisy—if they could write, that is.

Hans Can't they?

Sylvester *(sitting on the log)* Of course not—they're not old enough.

Hank and Hunk cross and stand behind Sylvester

Hans I meant did they tell you anything useful to *us*—like how to get to where Daisy lives, for instance?

Sylvester Oh, yes; I can tell you that. Now, you go through this clump of bushes ... Er—by the way, do you know this forest at all?

Hans I'm afraid not.

Sylvester Ah, well, that makes a difference. Look, do you see that ... ? No, you can't see it from here. *(He rises)* I think the only thing for it is to take you there.

Hans That's most kind of you, but we don't want to put you out ...

Sylvester Oh, it's all right. It's only a *few* miles out of our way. *(He fixes the ribbons to Hank and Hunk)*

Hans and the Princess move UC

I'll just put their ribbons on again, so they don't catch cold. They're delicate, you know. Inbreeding, I expect. There, now. If you'll kindly follow me.

Sylvester is starting to lead the way, when a woman's voice, very musical, is heard calling

Queen *(off; calling)* Syl-vest-er!

Sylvester Oh, dear, that's rather spoilt it, I'm afraid. I shan't be able to go with you after all.

Queen *(off; calling)* Syl-vest-er!

Sylvester *(calling)* Com-ing. *(To Hans)* I shall have to go.
Princess Whose was the voice?
Sylvester That's the Queen—the Queen of the Forest, you know.
Princess Where is she?
Sylvester Actually, she's invisible. We are, too, normally, only it happens to be Leap Year. Now, look, what you'd better do is to strike east—keep the sun on your right all the time. You won't go far wrong, and I'll try and catch you up later. How's that?

Hans and the Princess cross DR *and turn*

Hans That's fine, only—you won't forget, will you?
Sylvester I won't forget. Bye now. *(To Hank and Hunk)* Wave to the lady and gentleman. Bye.

Hank and Hunk wave

Hans and the Princess wave in reply and exit DR

What a dull couple. Nice, though, in their way.

Sylvester leads Hank and Hunk off DL. *Daisy, highly delighted with herself, enters* UL

Daisy Interesting. Very very interesting. And they think Daisy doesn't know. *(She moves* DC*)* But they don't know Daisy. Not on your sweet life, they don't. *(She crosses and looks off* DR*)* There they go, tripping through the trees, all on their way to call on Daisy in Daisy's little cottage. *(She moves* C*)* Ah, but Daisy won't be there, and neither will Daisy's little cottage. "And why?" did you say? "Ah, why, ah, why," cried the rhubarb pie, "why was I baked so long?" Because Daisy is going to flit—to move house—every last brick of it. Oh, elusive little Daisy. *(She circles* R *and goes* UC*)* Where would be a suitable spot to which to translate me little ménage? Where's the last place they would look for me? Why here, of course. A delightful, secluded spot and no ground rent. And therefore and forthwith and without more ado—a spell. *(She recites)*
        "Hey diddle diddle, the ends and the middle,
        The kettle, the pot and the broom,
        Lift and take it and—careful don't break it,
        And set it down there with a boom,
        Set it down there with a boom, for Daisy,
        Set it down there with a *boom*."

There is a puff of smoke and a clap of thunder as the cottage appears R. *The cottage*

is mounted on a truck and is run in on tracks above the middle wing R. *It is like Teapot Hall, all roof and no wall, and quite as crazy as its owners in its lineaments. It has a tiny door* R *and a small window* L. *Over the door is a neat little notice in pokerwork: "En-dor Cottage. Potions while you wait"*

There we are. Now, just to make sure the fire's in.

Daisy goes into the cottage and shuts the door. Smoke begins to come out of the chimney. Daisy pops out again

Botheration! Of course I *would* forget to charm the firewood here as well as the fire. That means I'll have to collect some more. Double botheration!

Daisy trots off UL

Castor enters cautiously DR

Castor (*over his shoulder*) Sh! Don't make so much noise, Senna.

Senna enters DR

Where's your woodcraft!
Senna I can't help it. I hate forests, anyway. They're too damp. My feet are all wet.
Castor They're not the only part of you that's all wet.
Senna (*moving below Castor to* C) I think I'm getting pneumonia. (*He coughs*) I'm sure I'm getting it. I'm going back.
Castor (*restraining Senna*) Senna, we've got to find the Princess's memory, and we've got to find it first. Now, pull yourself together.
Senna You wouldn't have a couple of aspirins on you, I suppose?
Castor No, I wouldn't.
Senna You might at least take my temperature.
Castor I've no thermometer.
Senna Or my pulse. Take my hand.
Castor No. I've no watch.
Senna You're just being beastly to me. (*He stamps on Castor's foot*)
Castor Oh, for heaven's sake! Look, you can't have pneumonia here. You must wait till we get home again, then you can have the doctor.
Senna (*crossing to the cottage*) Look, there's a cottage.
Castor So there is. (*He moves to Senna*)
Senna They might have some aspirin. Shall I go and ask?
Castor Wait! *This* is Daisy's cottage.
Senna Oh, Castor. Do you think so?
Castor (*moving* LC) I'm sure, but we must be careful. Daisy's dangerous.

Senna moves to Castor

You'd better go and see if she's in.

Senna moves towards the cottage, then stops and returns to Castor

Senna Why me?
Castor One of us has to go. Besides, you're more expendable.
Senna (*moving to* R *of the tree*) You hate me. You just want to be rid of me.
Castor Oh, all right, we'll both go. (*He moves towards the cottage*) Come on.

Senna follows Castor

Peep through the window, first.

They creep to the window and look inside

Senna Can't see anybody. But look at all those bottles. A regular dispensary.

A slight cracking noise is heard off L

Castor Sh! I can hear someone in the wood.

Daisy's voice is heard, singing

It's Daisy. Hide round the back, quick.

Castor and Senna hide behind the cottage

Daisy enters L, *carrying a bundle of sticks which she deposits by the side of the cottage door*

Daisy Poof! I'm puffed. What a trail for a little bit of kindling. (*She straightens up and sniffs the air*) That's rum! (*She moves* DR *and sniffs*) Very rum. Rum ti tum tum, an unusual hum. Mothballs? Eucalyptus? (*She crosses to* L) No, but equally clinical——

Senna and Castor peer out

—equally finickal, antiseptically prophylactical. (*She turns*)

Senna and Castor hide

Oh, what lovely long words Daisy does *know.* (*She crosses to* C) A fig for Roedean.

Somebody nasty has been around. Well, they're not around now, so we'll forget 'em. (*She moves to the cottage*) Now, for a nice little cup of nettle tea.

Daisy picks up the wood and goes into the cottage. Smoke puffs out of the chimney

Castor and Senna peep out, then cautiously approach the door, but hastily retreat behind the cottage

Daisy reappears carrying a stool with a cup of tea and a glass phial on it. She stops and switches her eyeballs to left and right suspiciously

What was that? (*She pauses*) Nothing—probably Lucy. Lucy Nation. (*She moves* c) She often plays little tricks on Daisy. But Daisy don't mind. She knows a trick or two herself. And here's one of her favourites. (*She sets the stool c, picks up the phial and cup of tea, settles herself comfortably on the stool, sips the tea, gazes into the phial and sighs*) Now for my daily gloat. People wonder why I steal memories. I steal them because—because—(*she sniffs in self-pity*) I never had no childhood—any childhood—born full-grown out of a thorn-bush when a flash of lightning struck it. Never played hopscotch like she's doing now—and she's so pretty. I might have been as pretty as that, you know—and as happy—happy as the day is long, I was—she was, I mean. Are they her memories or are they mine? Mine. They're mine, I say; all mine; happy, happy days so long ago. (*She suddenly shakes herself out of it*) Steady, Daisy—steady, girl; mustn't give way to sentiment too much—that way sanity lies, and who'd be sane, I'd like to know? Mustn't overdo it. (*She suddenly rises*) Oh, brambles and buttermilk! I've left the kettle on, burning its copper bottom out, wither it!

Daisy puts down the phial and exits hurriedly to the cottage, taking the teacup with her

Castor and Senna emerge at once, much excited

Castor Did you hear what she was saying, Senna?
Senna I heard it, but I didn't understand it. That woman only speaks one sensible word in three.
Castor She meant ... (*He sees the phial*) Look. She's left it behind.
Senna Left what behind?
Castor The phial with the Princess's memory.
Senna Are you sure?
Castor Of course. (*He picks up the phial*) Look for yourself. (*He gazes into the phial*) See, there's the Princess herself—but it's a long time ago. She must have been about fourteen.
Senna Yes, yes; I see her. (*He moves to the log and sits*) I remember—it was the day she was given the white pony for her birthday.

Castor (*moving and sitting beside Senna on the log*) She's giving it sugar. Oh, that *was* a happy day for her.

Daisy, unseen by the other two, comes out of the cottage, carrying her butterfly net, and creeps up behind them

I remember it well—the King had sacked us twice that morning.
Daisy (*making two snatches with the net in the air above their heads*) Snip, snap.

Senna and Castor relapse into amnesia

Got 'em. Thought they'd get the better of Daisy, eh? Lovely, lovely! Always works, it does. I'll take that, thank you. (*She takes the phial from Castor's unresisting hand*) Phew! Nearly lost it that time, though. We'll have you back inside where it's safer.

Daisy bustles into the cottage and returns minus the phial and net, but carrying a bowl of onions and two knives

(*Crossing to Castor and Senna*) We must give you something to do. Can't have you idle, you know. And daily help is just what I've been short of. Oh, clever little Daisy. (*To Castor*) Here, you. What do you think I keep you for?
Castor What? What did you say?
Daisy Haven't forgotten who *I* am, by any chance, have you?
Castor You? Why, yes, I ...
Daisy And who *you* are?
Castor Who *am* I?
Daisy You're the staff.
Senna Staff?
Daisy The lackeys, the scullions, the skivvies. Here. (*She thrusts the bowl at them*)
Castor (*taking the bowl*) What's this?
Daisy Peel 'em.
Senna Peel them?
Daisy Then slice 'em.
Castor Slice them?
Daisy Then make them into soup for my supper.
Castor ⎫ (*together*) Soup?
Senna ⎭
Daisy Soup. *Potage. Potage à l'oignon.* Delicious. Daisy's favourite dish. And sharp's the word.

Castor and Senna start to peel the onions

(*She crosses to the cottage*) Onion soup. Mmmmmm! I can hardly wait. (*She turns*) Beautiful soup!

Castor ⎤ (*together*) Beautiful, beautiful, *beautiful soup!*
Senna ⎦

Daisy goes into the cottage

Castor and Senna continue peeling in silence. Very soon they begin to cry, softly at first, then loudly and unrestrainedly as the Lights fade

HARD TIMES
Adapted by Stephen Jeffreys
from the novel by Charles Dickens

In this adaptation of Charles Dickens's classic, the Prologue sets the atmosphere of an industrial town in Lancashire in the1840s, and the characters of Tom Gradgrind and Sissy Jupe immediately come to life in the schoolroom. As with all Dickens's characters, these are boldly drawn: Mr Bounderby, the self-made man, Louisa and her feckless brother, Tom, and Mrs Sparsit, so aptly named. As Stephen Jeffreys writes in the introduction: 'In order to sustain the momentum of the story, it is necessary to keep the action moving continuously, so designers should aim for simplicity and speed ...'

Set: A bare stage for the opening scene and minimal furniture for the following scenes. Period: 1840s.

Cast: M2 F2.
In the original production the parts were divided between two actors and two actresses as follows: Actor 1: Bounderby, a self-made man, friend to Gradgrind. Actor 2: Gradgrind, proprietor of the model school, later MP/Tom, Gradgrind's son. Actress 1: Sissy Jupe, a stroller's daughter, earlier abandoned by her father/Mrs Sparsit, keeper of Bounderby's house. Actress 2: Louisa, Gradgrind's daughter.

Playing time: 16 minutes.

SCENE A

A bare stage

Five minutes or so before the show goes up, the actors come on and chat with the audience. Then the following is chanted to signal the beginning of the play

Solo   Good people all, both great and small,
            Come listen to my rhymes;
            I'll sing to you a verse or two
            Concerning of the times:

All   The Cotton Lords of Lancashire
                     Are plucking up their feathers;
                     They are a mob, so help me Bob,
                     Of humbugs altogether.

                     There never was such hard times seen in England before.

The following is then spoken as a chorus:

Actor 1 Coketown.
Actress 1 A triumph of fact.
Actor 2 Coketown.
Actress 2 A place devoid of fancy.
Actor 1 Coketown.
Actress 1 A town of brick that would have been red if the smoke and ashes had
  allowed it.
Actor 2 Coketown.
Actress 2 A town of unnatural red and black like the face of a painted savage.
Actor 1 A town of machinery and tall chimneys, out of which interminable serpents
  of smoke trailed themselves for ever and ever and never got uncoiled.
Actress 1 A town with a black canal and a river that ran purple with ill-smelling dye.
Actor 2 Vast piles of buildings full of windows where there was a rattling and a
  trembling all day long ...
Actress 2 And where the piston of the steam-engine worked monotonously up and
  down like the head of an elephant in a state of melancholy madness.
Actor 1 A town inhabited by children all very like one another ...
Actress 1 Parts of the Coketown machine ...
Actor 2 Stripped of all fancy ...
Actress 2 Shaped on the anvil of fact ...
Actor 1 Worked in the furnace of fact ...
Actress 1 Turned out in that great factory of fact ...
Actor 2 Mr Gradgrind's model school.
Actress 1 *Hard Times* by Charles Dickens.

SCENE B

Actor 1 Time went on in Coketown like its own machinery: so much material
  wrought up, so much fuel consumed, so many powers worn out, so much money
  made. But, less inexorable than iron, steel or brass, it brought its varying seasons
  even into that wilderness of smoke and brick, and made the only stand that ever
  was made in the place against its direful uniformity. Time passed Tom on into
  Bounderby's bank, made him an inmate of Bounderby's house, necessitated the
  purchase of his first razor, and exercised him diligently in his calculations relative

to number one. That same great manufacturer, Time, passed Sissy onwards in his mill, and worked her up into a very pretty article indeed.

Sissy and Gradgrind come on

Gradgrind I fear, Jupe, that your continuance any longer at the school would be useless.
Sissy I'm afraid it would, sir. I have tried hard, sir.
Gradgrind I believe you have. You are an affectionate, earnest, good young woman, and we must make that do.
Sissy I should wish for nothing if only my father——
Gradgrind That will do, Jupe! If your training in the science of reason had been more successful, we would long ago have heard the last on that subject.

Sissy and Gradgrind go

Actor 1 In some stages of his manufacture of the human fabric, the processes of time are very rapid. Tom and Sissy being both at such a stage in their working up, these changes were effected in a year or two: while Mr Gradgrind himself seemed stationary in his course and underwent no alteration, except that Time hustled him into a dirty by-corner, and made him Member of Parliament for Coketown. He also, at this time, made a discovery.

Gradgrind enters. Louisa comes on from the other side of the stage. She walks slowly across Gradgrind's field of vision

Gradgrind   Louisa is becoming a young woman.
                     Louisa is a young woman.
                     Louisa is a woman.

Louisa is now there, with Gradgrind

My dear. I must speak with you alone and seriously. Come to me in my room at breakfast tomorrow, will you?
Louisa Yes Father.

Gradgrind goes

So he kissed her and went away, and Louisa returned to the fireside to look at the short-lived sparks which so soon subsided into ashes.

Louisa sits. The Lights close in around her. Pause

(*To herself*) Dear Tom.

Tom's voice (*from off stage, as if in her thoughts*) It would do me a great deal of good if you were to make up your mind to I know what, Loo. It would be a splendid thing for me. It would be uncommonly jolly.

The Lights come up. Gradgrind is standing in his study. Louisa sits, listening

Gradgrind Louisa my dear, you are the subject of a proposal of marriage that has been made to me.

Pause

A proposal of marriage, my dear.

Louisa I am attending, Father.

Gradgrind Perhaps you are not unprepared for the announcement I have it in charge to make.

Louisa I cannot say that, Father, until I hear it. Prepared or unprepared, I wish to hear it all from you. I wish to hear you state it to me.

Gradgrind Well then ... I have undertaken to let you know that ... that Mr Bounderby has informed me that he has long watched your progress with particular interest and pleasure, and has long hoped that the time might ultimately arrive when he should offer you his hand in marriage. That time is now come. Mr Bounderby has made his proposal of marriage to me, and has entreated me to make it known to you, and to express his hope that you will take it into your favourable consideration.

Silence

Louisa Father. Do you think I love Mr Bounderby?

Pause

Gradgrind My child ... I really cannot take it upon myself to say.

Louisa Father, do you ask me to love Mr Bounderby?

Gradgrind My dear Louisa. (*He pauses*) No. I ask nothing.

Louisa Father. Does Mr Bounderby ask me to love him?

Gradgrind Really my dear, it is difficult to answer your question ...

Louisa Yes or no, Father?

Gradgrind Difficult, because ... because the reply depends so materially on the sense in which we use the expression. Mr Bounderby does not do you the injustice of pretending to anything fanciful, fantastic or sentimental. In these circumstances, the expression you used may be a little misplaced.

Louisa What would you advise me to use in its stead, Father?

Gradgrind I would advise you to consider the question, as you have been accustomed to consider every other question, simply as one of tangible Fact——

Louisa What would you recommend, Father, that I should substitute for the term I used just now? For the ... misplaced expression?

Gradgrind Louisa. Nothing can be plainer. Confine yourself rigidly to Fact. The question of Fact to state to yourself is: "Does Mr Bounderby ask me to marry him?" Answer: "Yes, he does." The sole remaining question then is: "Shall I marry him?" I think nothing can be plainer than that.

Louisa "Shall I marry him?"

Gradgrind Precisely.

A pause. Louisa stares out of the window

Louisa The Coketown chimneys. There seems to be nothing there but smoke. But when night comes ... the fire ... bursts out ...

Gradgrind Louisa. Louisa. What is the application of that remark?

Louisa What does it matter? What does it matter? Since Mr Bounderby likes to take me thus, I am satisfied to accept his proposal. Tell him, as soon as you please, that this was my answer. Repeat it word for word. I should wish him to know what I said.

Gradgrind I will observe your request, my dear. It is quite right to be exact. Have you any wish as to the date of your wedding?

Louisa None. What does it matter?

Pause

Gradgrind Louisa. I have not considered it essential to ask one question because the possibility implied in it appeared to me to be much too remote. But perhaps I ought to do so. You have never entertained in secret any other proposal?

Louisa What other proposal can have been made to me? Whom have I seen? Where have I been? What are my heart's experiences?

Pause

Gradgrind You correct me justly. I merely wished to discharge my duty.

Louisa What do I know of tastes and fancies; of aspirations and affections; of all that part of my nature in which such light things might have been nourished? What escape have I had from problems that could be demonstrated and realities that could be grasped? (*She tightens her hand, then slowly unclenches it*) What a question to ask *me*? You have been so careful of me that I never had a child's heart. You have trained me so well that I never dreamed a child's dream. You have dealt so wisely with me that I never had a child's belief or a child's fear.

Gradgrind My dear Louisa. You abundantly repay my care. Kiss me, my dear girl.

She kisses him

Now. Let us go and find your mother.

They go

Then Louisa breaks away

Gradgrind exits

Louisa (*out front*) Mrs Gradgrind was accordingly found and informed, the news occasioning feeble signs of animation in her recumbent form. But Sissy, who was working beside her and heard of the engagement in the same instant, suddenly turned her head and looked, in wonder, in pity, in sorrow, in doubt, in a multitude of emotions towards Louisa. Louisa had known it, and seen it, without looking at her. From that moment, she was impassive, proud and cold—held Sissy at a distance—changed to her altogether.

Louisa goes

Actor 1 comes on immediately

SCENE C

Actor 1 Mr Bounderby's first disquietude, on hearing of his happiness, was occasioned by the necessity of imparting it to Mrs Sparsit. He could not make up his mind how to do that, or what the consequences of the step might be. Whether she would instantly depart bag and baggage to Lady Scadgers, or would positively refuse to budge from the premises; whether she would break her heart or break the looking-glass, Mr Bounderby could not at all foresee. On his way home, on the evening he set aside for telling her this momentous news, he took the precaution of stepping into a chemist's shop and buying a bottle of the very strongest smelling salts. "By George," thought Mr Bounderby, "if she takes it in the fainting way, I'll have the skin off her nose at all events." But in spite of being thus forearmed, he entered his own house with anything but a courageous air, and appeared before the object of his misgivings like a dog who was conscious of coming direct from the pantry.

He becomes Bounderby. Mrs Sparsit is sitting by the fire, picking holes in a piece of cambric with the points of her scissors

Mrs Sparsit Good-evening, Mr Bounderby.
Bounderby Good-evening, ma'am, good-evening.

Bounderby draws his chair close to the fire. Mrs Sparsit draws hers further away

Don't go to the North Pole, ma'am.

Mrs Sparsit Thank you, sir. (*She moves her chair back, though short of its former position*)

Bounderby Mrs Sparsit, ma'am. I have no occasion to say to you, that you are not only a lady born and bred, but a devilish sensible woman.

Mrs Sparsit Sir, this is not the first time that you have honoured me with similar expression of your good opinion.

Bounderby Mrs Sparsit ma'am. I am going to astonish you. (*He is on his feet, reaching for the stopper for the smelling salts, concealed behind his back*)

Mrs Sparsit (*calmly*) Yes sir? (*She lays down her work and smooths her mittens*)

Bounderby I am going, ma'am, to marry Tom Gradgrind's daughter.

Mrs Sparsit (*immediately*) Yes sir? I hope you may be happy, Mr Bounderby. I hope indeed you may be happy.

Bounderby, who has the stopper off the smelling salts and is ready to administer them, is astonished by her tranquillity, and furtively conceals the bottle

Bounderby Ah!

Mrs Sparsit Yes sir, I wish with all my heart that you may, in all respects, be very happy.

Bounderby Well, ma'am. I am obliged to you. I hope I shall be.

Mrs Sparsit *Do* you sir? But naturally you do. Of course you do.

Pause. Mrs Sparsit resumes her work. She coughs in a small, triumphant way

Bounderby Well, ma'am, under these circumstances, I imagine it would not be agreeable to a character like yours to remain here. Though you would, of course, be very welcome. If you did.

Mrs Sparsit Oh dear, no sir. I could on no account think of that. (*She coughs again*)

Bounderby However, ma'am, there are apartments at the bank where a born and bred lady as keeper of the place would be rather a catch than otherwise; and if the same terms——

Mrs Sparsit I beg your pardon, sir. You were so good as to promise that you would always substitute the phrase "annual compliment".

Bounderby I apologize, ma'am. Annual compliment. If the same annual compliment would be acceptable there, I see nothing to part us—unless you do.

Mrs Sparsit Sir, if the position I should assume at the bank is one that I could occupy without descending lower in the social scale——

Bounderby Why of course it is. If it was not, you would not suppose I would offer it to a lady who has moved in the society you have moved in.

Mrs Sparsit You are very considerate, sir.

Bounderby You'll have your own private apartments, a maid and a light porter, and you'll be what I take the liberty of considering precious comfortable.

Mrs Sparsit Sir, say no more. I accept your offer gratefully and with many sincere acknowledgements of past favours. And I hope sir, I fondly hope, that Miss Gradgrind may be all you desire and deserve. (*She beams at him*)

The Lights fade, then come up immediately

SCENE D

The wedding. All available actors become wedding guests

Actress 1 And so the day came: and when it came, there were married ...
Actor 1 Josiah Bounderby of Coketown ...
Actress 2 To Louisa ...
Actor 2 Daughter of Thomas Gradgrind Esquire of Stone Lodge, MP for that borough.

Bounderby and Louisa in a wedding tableau. Cries of "Speech, speech." Bounderby takes centre stage perhaps standing on a raised platform or chair. Louisa stands watching him. The other actors melt into the audience, who become wedding guests. Bounderby holds up a hand

Bounderby Ladies and gentlemen. I am Josiah Bounderby of Coketown. If you want a speech this morning, my friend and father-in-law, Tom Gradgrind, is a Member of Parliament, so you know where to get it.

Laughter

I am not your man. Still, since you have done my wife and myself the honour of drinking our health and happiness, I suppose I must acknowledge the same. (*He clears his throat*) If I feel a little independent when I look around this gathering today, and reflect how little I thought of marrying Tom Gradgrind's daughter when I was a ragged street-boy who never washed his face unless it was at a pump, and that not oftener than once a fortnight, I hope I may be excused. So I hope you like my feeling independent; if you don't, I can't help it. I *do* feel independent.

Laughter

Now I have mentioned and you have mentioned that I am this day married to Tom Gradgrind's daughter. I am very glad to be so. I believe she is worthy of me. And I believe I am worthy of her. So I thank you, on both our parts, for the goodwill you have shown towards us: and the best wish I can give the unmarried part of the present company is this: I hope every bachelor may find as good a wife as I have found. And I hope every spinster may find as good a husband as my wife has found. Thank you.
Actor 2 A toast to the bride and groom!

All The bride and groom!

Louisa joins her husband. Tableau

Actress 1 Shortly after which oration, as they were going on a nuptial trip to Lyons, the happy pair departed for the railroad.

Bounderby goes off

The bride in passing down the stairs found Tom waiting for her.

Tom comes forward, flushed with drink. He has a brandy glass and a cigar

Tom What a game girl you are, Loo, to be such a first-rate sister!

She holds him tightly, her feelings only just in check

Come on now. Time's up. Old Bounderby's quite ready. Goodbye, I shall be on the look-out for you, when you come back. My dear Loo, an't it uncommonly jolly now! (*He moves away*) An't it uncommonly jolly!

He goes

Louisa stands, alone. She stares ahead. The Lights fade

HIAWATHA
by Michael Bogdanov

Adapted from Longfellow's poem, this is a fast-moving, visual play with dance, mime and music with percussion. The scenes are linked by a storyteller, who could be more than one speaker. Nokomis has raised her grandson, Hiawatha, who marries Minnehaha. In this, the final part of the play, Famine and Fever arrive to take Minnehaha away, and the burial ceremony takes place. Then Hiawatha, dying alone, sees the vision of the White Man and with the help of the Company, he moves away on his canoe. The play offers scope for originality and challenge in presentation, involving a flexible cast.

Set:
In the Royal National Theatre's production the setting was the framework of a giant tepee, so that there was circular floor space for all the action. In the background hung a large circular disc which, lit from behind, created the impression of moonlight, sunset, daylight, etc. Period: legendary.

Cast: flexible.
Hiawatha, now the grown-up Indian. Minnehaha, his wife. Fever and Famine, in black cloaks and masks. Chibiabos, the singer. Kwasind, the Strong Man. Nokomis, Hiawatha's grandmother. Iagoo, the Great Boaster. Cavalry Officer, the dreaded white man. Story-teller. Chorus.

Playing time: 16 minutes.

THE FAMINE

Story-Teller   O the long and dreary winter!
                     O the cold and cruel winter!

Some of the Company lay poles on the floor, creating the effect of the cross poles of a tepee. One by one, the Company lay the white cloaks across the poles

                     Ever thicker, thicker, thicker,
                     Froze the ice on lake and river,

Ever deeper, deeper, deeper
Fell the snow o'er all the landscape,
Fell the covering snow and drifted
Through the forest, round the village.

Chibiabos and Kwasind don black blankets and walk past the Story-Teller during the following

Gone was gentle Chibiabos,
Gone the gentle strong-man Kwasind,
To the islands of the Blessed,
To the land of ghosts and shadows.

Minnehaha lies in the centre of the stage

All the earth was sick and famished,
Hungry was the air around them,
Hungry was the sky above them,
And the hungry stars in heaven
Like the eyes of wolves glared at them!

Two red pinspots of light appear in the gloom. Strange, eerie sounds are heard. Hiawatha kneels by Minnehaha

Came two guests, of gloom and silence
Looked with haggard eyes and hollow
At the face of Laughing Water.

Two members of the Company, dressed as Fever and Famine, approach

Famine   Behold me!
            I am Famine, Bukadawin!
Fever   Behold me!
            I am Fever, Ahkosewin!

Nokomis kneels by Minnehaha

Story-Teller   And the lovely Minnehaha
            Shuddered as they looked upon her,
            Lay there, trembling, freezing, burning.

Hiawatha ascends to the higher level

	Forth into the empty forest,
	Rushed the maddened Hiawatha.
Hiawatha	Gitche Manito, the Mighty!
	Give us food, or we must perish!
	Give me food for Minnehaha,
	For my dying Minnehaha!

Fever and Famine beckon to Minnehaha

Story-Teller	But there came no other answer
	Than the echo of the woodlands,
Company (*whispering*)	
	Minnehaha! Minnehaha!
Minnehaha	Hark! I hear a rushing,
	Hear a roaring and a rushing,
	Hear the Falls of Minnehaha
	Calling to me from a distance.
Nokomis	No, my child,
	'Tis the night-wind in the pine trees!
Minnehaha	Look! I see my father
	Standing lonely at his doorway,
	Beckoning to me from his wigwam,
	In the land of the Dacotahs!

The Story-Teller comes slowly from the back with a long white pole

Nokomis	No, my child!
	'Tis the smoke that waves and beckons!
Minnehaha	Ah! the eyes of Pauguk
	Glare upon me in the darkness;
	I can feel his icy fingers
	Clasping mine amid the darkness!

Minnehaha grasps the white pole, which gradually slips from her fingers. Minnehaha falls back

Company (*whispering*)	
	Hiawatha! Hiawatha!
Story-Teller	And the desolate Hiawatha,
	Far away amid the forest,
	Heard the voice of Minnehaha.
Company (*whispering*)	
	Hiawatha! Hiawatha!

Story-Teller   And he rushed into the wigwam,
Saw his lovely Minnehaha
Lying dead and cold before him;
Uttered such a cry of anguish,
That the very stars in heaven
Shook and trembled with his anguish.

The Company wrap white fur round Minnehaha

Nokomis   Then they buried Minnehaha;
In the snow a grave they made her,
Covered her with snow, like ermine,
Thus they buried Minnehaha.

The Company lift Minnehaha in the air on crossed poles. A lighting effect of a fire comes up downstage

Story-Teller   And at night a fire was lighted,
On her grave four times was kindled,
For her soul upon its journey
To the islands of the Blessed.

The Company parade round holding Minnehaha high in the air to the accompaniment of a drumbeat. Minnehaha is lowered to the floor and the furs are unwrapped. The furs and poles are struck

There is a roll of drums. The Lights change. The Company sit in a semi-circle. Iagoo circles the stage then stops c

THE WHITE MAN'S FOOT

Story-Teller   From his wanderings far to eastward,
From the regions of the morning,
Homeward now returned Iagoo,
The greater traveller, the greater boaster,
Full of new and strange adventures.

Iagoo   I have seen a water
Bigger than the Big Sea Water,
Broader than the Gitche Gumee,
Bitter so that none could drink it!

All   It cannot be so!
It cannot be so!

Iagoo   O'er it, o'er this water
Came a great canoe with pinions,

	A canoe with wings came flying,
	Bigger than a grove of pine-trees
	Taller than the tallest tree-tops!
All	We don't believe it!
	We don't believe it!
Iagoo	From its mouth to greet him
	Came Waywassimo, the lightning,
	Came the thunder, Annemeekee!
All	What tales you tell us!
Iagoo	In it, came a people,
	In the great canoe with pinions
	Came a hundred warriors,
	Painted white were all their faces,
	And with hair their chins were covered.
All	What lies you tell us!
	Do not think that we believe him!
Story-Teller	Only Hiawatha laughed not,
	But he gravely spake and answered
	To their jeering and their jesting:

Hiawatha stands with Iagoo

Hiawatha   True is all Iagoo tells us;

The shadow of a Cavalry Officer appears on the white disc. The drummer plays a military march on a snare drum, faintly

    I have seen it in a vision,
    Seen the great canoe with pinions,
    Seen the people with white faces,
    Seen the coming of this bearded
    People of the wooden vessel
    From the regions of the morning,
    From the shining land of Wabun.
    Gitche Manito the Mighty
    Sends them to us with his message.
    Let us welcome then the strangers,
    Hail them as our friends and brothers.

The shadow fades

    I beheld, too, in that vision,
    All the secrets of the future,

All the land was full of people,
Restless, struggling, toiling, striving,
In the woodlands rang their axes,
Smoked their towns in all the valleys,
Over all the lakes and rivers,
Rushed their great canoes of thunder.

The Cavalry Officer appears on a higher level in front of the white disc

I beheld our nations scattered,
Weakened, warring with each other,
Saw the remnants of our people
Sweeping westward, wild and woeful,
Like the cloud-rack of a tempest,
Like the withered leaves of Autumn!

The drumbeats build to a climax. The Cavalry Officer turns towards the audience and fires his revolver. There is the sound of thunder. A flute plays. Two of the Company hold poles, crossed, downstage. Hiawatha moves downstage and stands in front of the crossed poles; the rest of the Company stand behind him

HIAWATHA'S DEPARTURE

Story-Teller   By the shore of Gitche Gumee,
By the shining Big Sea Water,
At the doorway of his wigwam,
In the pleasant summer morning,
Hiawatha stood and waited.
Stood and waited for death to take him.
Toward the sun his hands were lifted,
Both the palms spread out against it,
And between the parted fingers
Fell the sunshine on his features.

Hiawatha   I am going, O my people,
On a long and distant journey;
Many moons and many winters
Will have come, and will have vanished,
Ere I come again and see you.
White man's foot I leave behind me;
Listen to the words of wisdom,
Listen to the truth they tell you,
For the Master of Life has sent them,
From the land of light and morning.

Members of the Company bring the canoe downstage

Story-Teller   On the shore stood Hiawatha,
Turned and waved his hand at parting;
On the clear and luminous water
Launched his birch canoe for sailing,

Hiawatha gets in the canoe

Whispered to it: "Westward! Westward!"
And with speed it darted forward.

The Company lift the canoe and place it on the higher level. The Story-Teller kneels downstage

And the evening sun descending
Set the clouds in fire with redness,
Burned a broad sky, like a prairie,
Left upon the level water
One long track and trail of splendour,

The Company turn to face upstage, their hands in the air. Hiawatha moves up in front of the white disc. There is the sound of the wind softly blowing

Down whose stream, as down a river,
Westward, westward Hiawatha
Sailed into the fiery sunset,
Sailed into the purple vapours,
Sailed into the dusk of evening.

Thus departed Hiawatha,
Hiawatha the Beloved,
In the glory of the sunset,
In the purple mists of evening,
To the regions of the home-wind,
Of the North West Wind, Keewaydin,
To the islands of the Blessed,
To the land of the Hereafter!

The drums beat as the Company stomp off, the sound gradually dying

HIJACK OVER HYGENIA
A scene adapted from the play by David Wood

A villainous Measle has landed illegally in the spotless palace of Hygenia, the cleanest kingdom in the world. The Court agrees that Stainless, the Cat, should be left in charge to watch out for the dangerous intruder. Stainless is terrified.

Set: The corridor outside Princess Spotless's bedroom and Princess Spotless's bedroom.

Cast: M6 F4.
Stainless, the Cat, made of stainless steel for bravery, but now terrified of the untoward because Hygenia is so clean there are no mice or rats left. Should be played by a female. Measle, an unpleasant germ; looks like a cross between a mouse and a weasel. Princess Spotless, plain, plaited, whiny, bespectacled daughter of the King and Queen. Auntie Septic, an elderly aerosol spray, devoted to her duty to keep everything germ-free. Queen Clean of Hygenia, fat, chocolate-loving, bossy wife of King Spring. King Spring of Hygenia, obsessed by the cleanliness of his Kingdom; pompous, cowardly, but respected. Grime Minister, highest official of the government of Hygenia, carries an ornate broom as staff of office. The Court Duster, new recruit to the Palace team supposed to tell clean jokes while polishing. Gadget, odd-job man and part inventor, well meaning, prone to mistakes, short-sighted, wears spectacles; elderly. Doctor Spicknspan, mid-European hygiene expert attached to the Court.

Playing time: 19 minutes.

The corridor outside Princess Spotless's bedroom. This could be represented by the front area of the stage divided from the Princess's bedroom by a curtain or by lighting

Stainless is discovered trembling

After a pause, Princess Spotless enters on tiptoe, having escaped from her protective parents for a moment. Princess Spotless taps Stainless on the shoulder, who jumps with terror. She calms him down

Princess Spotless It's only me. (*Whispering*) Come and see me later. The door will
be open. Please.

Princess Spotless dashes off

*Stainless starts his guard duty. He walks one way, then turns the other, looking out
for the danger. When he reaches one side of the stage, he turns and walks towards the
other*

*As Stainless does this, Measle enters and follows him, walking warily backwards
and therefore unaware of Stainless's presence*

*Suddenly Measle and Stainless both sense danger, and stop. By this time the audience
may be shouting a warning. Gingerly, Stainless and Measle walk in a circle, round
each other, still back to back. Then they part, both walking forwards away from each
other. They see nothing, then walk backwards towards each other. They cross each
other, without touching, and turn slightly so that they are once again back to back,
going round in a circle. All these movements are punctuated with tense sensings of
danger. Now both relax, thinking they must have been mistaken. They back into each
other. Both jump, then freeze*

Measle runs in alarm and exits. Stainless, terrified, exits on the other side

The Lights fade and come up on the Princess's bedroom

There is a bed, bedside table and telephone and, facing upstage, a television

Princess Spotless enters with Auntie Septic. The Princess wears a nightie

Princess Spotless But Auntie Septic, I don't *want* to go to bed. It's not fair.
Auntie Septic I'm sorry, your Majesty. Emergency. The King commands, we all
obey. (*She sprays the bed*)
Princess Spotless Shan't.
Auntie Septic You must.
Princess Spotless Won't.
Auntie Spetic You will.
Princess Spotless Catch me, then.

*Auntie Septic chases her round the bed good-humouredly. Princess Spotless enjoys
this. She makes to go*

*The Queen enters carrying a bedtime drink, plus her own chocolates, which she
eats through the scene*

Princess Spotless bumps into her

Queen (*roaring*) Bed!
Princess Spotless (*meekly as a lamb*) Yes, Mummy. (*She climbs into bed*)

Auntie Septic fetches a tray of cleansing cream, gargle, etc.

Queen Inspection.

The Queen and Auntie Septic speak the following in a rhythmic routine

	Have you washed your hands?
Auntie Septic	Have you cleaned your teeth?
Queen	Have you rid your nails
Auntie Septic	Of the dirt that's underneath?
Queen	Have you brushed your hair?
Auntie Septic	Have you scrubbed behind your ears?

Queen
Auntie Septic } (*together*) Are you clean all over now, Spotless dear?
Princess Spotless (*fed up*)
                      Yes, I've washed my hands
                      Yes, I've cleaned my teeth
                      Yes, I've rid my nails
                      Of the dirt that's underneath
                      Yes, I've brushed my hair
                      Yes, I've scrubbed behind my ears
                      If I scrub much harder they'll disappear.

The Queen and Auntie Septic act out the words in unison as they speak

Queen   Rub in some cleansing cream
Auntie Septic   Get off all the grime
                     Now rub it off again
Princess Spotless What a waste of time!
Queen
Auntie Septic } (*together*) Aren't you just glad you're clean all over?
Princess Spotless I'm just glad — it's all over!

Auntie Septic picks up the tray

Auntie Septic Good-night, sleep tight, your Majesty.
Princess Spotless 'Night, Auntie Septic.

Auntie Septic exits

Mummy, will you read me a bedtime story?

Queen Sorry, Spotless, not tonight.

Princess Spotless But it's not fair. I *always* have a bedtime story.

Queen We don't *always* have enemies invading the Palace. So hurry up and down your bedtime drink and settle. Then I can turn the lights out.

As the Queen speaks, Measle enters furtively

Unseen by the Queen, who has her back to him, he deliberately takes a pill from a bottle and drops it into the bedtime drink. Audience reaction may try to warn the Queen and Princess Spotless, but they do not take any notice. The Queen turns round and, in the nick of time, Measle skedaddles under the bed. The Queen points sternly at the bedtime drink, and Princess Spotless, reluctantly, eventually drinks it. The Queen kisses her good-night and takes the glass

The Queen exits, turning off the light as she goes

Pause. Princess Spotless starts snoring. Measle emerges from the gloom, gleefully checks that the bedtime drink has been drunk, then goes to the telephone, dials a number, and waits. The following speech may be inaudible if the audience are still shouting a warning. In that case it should be mimed: "Mission successful"

Measle Hallo, Boss? M. One-o-one. Mission A accomplished. Over and out.

Measle exits

Princess Spotless snores even louder

After a few snores, Stainless enters tentatively

He shakes the Princess gently to wake her. She turns over sleepily to face him. He recoils in horror

Princess Spotless Hallo, Stainless. Stainless, what is it?

Stainless turns on the lights and fetches a mirror. He hands it to Princess Spotless, who looks into it and screams loudly. We see that she has huge spots all over her face

Spots! I've got *spots*! (*She screams again*)

Black-out, except, if possible, for a single spotlight focused on the television. As everyone sets up the next scene, the voice of a television announcer is heard

Announcer's voice This is a newsflash. A doctor is on his way to diagnose the Princess Spotless's mystery illness. She has been confined to her room. Meanwhile, the search goes on for the suspicious intruder, believed to have something to do with the Princess's sudden attack. You are all asked to look out for a creature of slight build, furry, and of a desperate character.

The Lights come up in the Princess's bedroom. It is the next morning

The King and Queen are at the bedside of the spotty Princess Spotless, anxiously comforting her

Auntie Septic sprays Princess Spotless. Concerned, Stainless watches. The Queen gorges chocolates from a box. There is a fanfare as:

The Grime Minister, Duster and Gadget enter. All are concerned

Duster carries a tray of small glasses which he hands round

Grime Minister (*announcing the Court's daily procedure*) The Royal Gargle.

All together, in a formal manner, gargle loudly, then drink. Duster collects up the glasses. Suddenly there is a loud knocking at the door

Duster, the door.

Duster goes to the door. In a moment he returns and whispers inaudibly to the Grime Minister that Doctor Spicknspan has arrived. Stainless tries to get nearer his mistress

Queen Stainless, stand aside. You're in disgrace.
King Fat lot of use you are, you cowardly cat.
Princess Spotless Don't bully him. He couldn't help it.
Queen No, and he *didn't* help, did he? Meant to be guarding us.
King Couldn't guard a tadpole.
Princess Spotless He raised the alarm.
Queen Only in fright.
Grime Minister (*announcing*) Doctor Spicknspan, your Majesties!

Doctor Spicknspan enters

Doctor Spicknspan Guten tag, bonjour, good-day. Was ist de matter, as zey say, jawohl?
King How do you do, Doctor. Welcome. Long time no see.
Doctor Spicknspan Ja. Ist long time since.
King We have all been so healthy.
Queen Till today. Our daughter has spots.
Doctor Spicknspan Spots? She is gespotty mit spotten? Ach so, how much?

King What?
Doctor Spicknspan How much?
King Oh, you mean how many? Spots? Oo, I suppose, seventeen, eighteen on her face, er ...
Doctor Spicknspan No, no, no, no, no. How much will you pay me? Ha, ha, ha. You make me vealthy, I make her healthy. Ha, ha, ha, zat is my motto.
King Ha, ha, ha. (*Slightly nervous*) The price is immaterial.
Queen She is our daughter.
Doctor Spicknspan Very good. Bitte stand from ze patient.

All move. The Doctor sets to work. The Doctor takes the Princess's arm

Pulse. Say ahh.

The Doctor places a thermometer in the Princess's mouth as she says "ahh". He nods in time with her pulse, which gets faster and faster. He stops, gets out a stethoscope, puts it on, and listens in. He apparently hears nothing and looks worried

Princess Spotless (*in bed, with the thermometer still in her mouth*) Lower down.
Doctor Spicknspan What?
Princess Spotless My heart is lower down.
Doctor Spicknspan Ich cannot you hear. (*He points to the stethoscope in his ears*)

Princess Spotless takes out the thermometer and grabs the end of the stethoscope

Princess Spotless (*shouting down it*) My heart is lower down!

The Doctor jumps with the noise, takes the thermometer, looks at it and shakes his head

King Well?
Doctor Spicknspan She has — *Measles.*

There is a general gasp of horror

> (*Rhythmically*)
> First you see the spots
> Feel your temp'rature rise
> Soon you're sticky and hot
> With a pain behind the eyes
> In three weeks it will be past
> But it's nasty while it lasts
> You must leave her —
> It's the fever!

It's a bodily disorder
Of a minor common order
She is striken
She is sick 'n'
She's contagious
It's a typical distemper
So you mustn't lose your temper
It's not serious

King   She's delirious
It's outrageous!

During the following, Measle enters unseen, except by the audience, and pops a pill in the Queen's chocolate box. He exits unnoticed

All   First you see the spots
Feel your temp'rature rise
Soon you're sticky and hot
With a pain behind the eyes
In three weeks it will be past
But it's nasty while it lasts
We must leave her —
It's the fever!

Doctor Spicknspan With a childish disposition
One is prone to this condition
She's infected
She's affected
By bacteria
It is true she is unhealthy
But your Majesty is wealthy
For a small fee
You can call me
And I'll clear her.

All   First you see the spots
Feel your temp'rature rise
Soon you're sticky and hot
With a pain behind the eyes
In three weeks it will be past
But it's nasty while it lasts
We must leave her —
It's the fever!

Doctor Spicknspan Ze Princess Spotless in her bed muss stay.
Queen I'll look after her. I'll just have my last choccy.

There is a possible audience reaction to stop her taking the pill, but she pays no attention and swallows it. She sits on the bed facing upstage. Stainless, too, goes to the bed to comfort Princess Spotless. Everyone else is looking gloomy

Doctor Spicknspan (*coming downstage*) May Ich interrupt zis mood of melancholia by collecting my fee?
King With pleasure. (*He waves to the Grime Minister to deal with it*)
Grime Minister (*joining Doctor Spicknspan downstage*) Doctor Spicknspan, the bill.
Doctor Spicknspan Five hundred Hygenian pounds.
King What?
Doctor Spicknspan Please.
King (*joining the others downstage*) Five hundred? Scandalous.
Doctor Spicknspan Do you want her to get better or not?
King But — five hundred?
Doctor Spicknspan Ich will much time have to spenden mit her. Leave it or take it.
King Very well.

There are screams from the bed. All turn. The Queen turns her head

Queen Look at me! Look at me! Spots!

Auntie Septic rushes to give her a spray

Doctor Spicknspan Go away, go away. Your Majesty, kommen mit me to your bedchamber, schnell, schnell before it is too late.

Doctor Spicknspan hustles the Queen off

King Before it's too late? What's he talking about? Grime Minister!
Grime Minister Your Majesty?
King This measles must be catching.
Grime Minister Could lead to an epidemic, your Majesty. There has been so little illness in Hygenia, your subjects will not be strong enough to withstand it.
King An epidemic?
Grime Minister It could spread like wildfire.
King What are we to do? *I* could be next.
Gadget Your Majesty, might I suggest a television appearance? It would make me so proud if my television system could help in any ——
King That's it. Speak to the Kingdom. Grime Minister, off you go. Tell our subjects to stay indoors. Measles must not take over Hygenia.
Grime Minister Maybe I should change my suit.
King Rubbish. This is an emergency.

The Grime Minister is pushed off

The others, hearing the King's last impassioned words, applaud his last line

(*Receiving the applause*) Thank you. (*He suddenly notices Duster standing there*) You, Court Duster. You've kept very quiet. I think you know more than meets the eye. I've never trusted you.

Duster But why not? I may be new, but I've done nothing — I haven't even told many jokes because of all this trouble. Why pick on me?

Auntie Septic (*calming him down*) Duster, that's enough. Your Majesty, I can vouch for Duster's true loyalty. You can be sure that both of us — and Gadget — will fight for Hygenia's safety — and your own.

Gadget Indeed, your Majesty, and this might perhaps be the moment to introduce my latest efforts towards the war against the unclean.

King Why certainly, Gadget.

Gadget The most up-to-date, super-duper, ultra-special, make-your-eyes-pop-out-on-stalks — washing machine.

Fanfare

Duster, Auntie Septic and Gadget go off and return leading on the mahcine

King Oh, how wonderful. A demonstration, please.

Duster Your Majesty, might I suggest — well, there is a danger — you see, your clothes may be infected.

King What? (*He immediately feels imaginary itches*)

Duster Infected with measles.

Auntie Septic Constant contact with the afflicted.

King Oooh. What can I do?

Gadget Wash them. In here. As part of the demonstration.

The King is unable to wait. Forgetting embarrassment, he starts to strip off

King Good idea. Infected? Ugh.

The King gingerly removes his outer garments, revealing funny underwear. As each garment comes off it is passed at arm's length along the line, eventually reaching Gadget, who pops it in the machine. When all the clothes are in Gadget turns the knobs

Gadget Hot wash, spin dry, starch, disinfectant — here goes. (*He switches on*)

Noisy rhythmic sounds are heard

(*Speaking rhythmically*)
                Rumble, rumble

> Toss, turn, tumble
> The water churns and round and about
> Rumble, rumble
> Toss, turn, tumble
> See the diff'rence as they all come out.

The machine stops — maybe a green light comes on. Gadget steps forward and removes a garment. It is as stiff as a board

King Gadget, what have you done?
Auntie Spetic Starch. Too much starch.
Gadget Apologies, your Majesty. Let's try again. (*Changing the switches accordingly and replacing the garment, he turns the knobs on again. Speaking rhythmically*)
> Rumble, rumble
> Toss, turn, tumble
> The water churns and round and about
> Rumble, rumble
> Toss, turn, tumble
> See the diff'rence as they all come out.

The machine stops. Gadget removes a garment, and another, and another — all are tiny

Duster Oh no, they've shrunk!
King Gadget, you bodger! They're ruined.
Gadget Apologies, apologies, your Majesty. (*He starts to push the machine off*) I'll take it back to the workshop. Oh dear, oh dear, oh dear ...

Gadget, terrified, exits with the machine

King And next time, test it with your own garments, and not the Royal Outfit number three. Hey, wait! Return! Turn on the telly. I want to view the Grime Minister's speech to the Kingdom.

Gadget sheepishly returns, switches on the television, then exits

Fanfare from the television. Duster and Auntie Septic stand to attention. The set then runs down with an awful sound. Then — nothing. Duster and Auntie Septic relax from the "attention" pose

King Don't say *that's* not working either. (*He bashes the set*)
Duster Can I help, your Majesty? (*He bashes the set too*)
King Can't understand it. All these spots all over the screen.

Realization registers. The King and Duster turn the television round to reveal a spotty screen

Spots!
Auntie Septic Measles!
Duster But that's impossible. Whoever heard of a measly telly?
King (*transfixed*) Stop talking. Telephone Gadget.

Duster goes to the telephone and dials

Duster The line's dead. It's out of order.
King What's going on? Hygenia is being slowly paralysed.
Auntie Septic I'll go and find Gadget, your Majesty.
King Thank you, Auntie Septic. Tell him it's an emergency. He's to go up on the roof and investigate the ailing telly and the failing phone.
Auntie Septic Straightaway, your Majesty.

Auntie Septic exits

The King realizes he is alone with Duster for the first time. He eyes him suspiciously

Duster Don't get in a paddy, your Majesty. I'll make you laugh.
King I don't feel like laughing.
Duster Listen to this. What's green and hairy and goes up and down?
King I don't know. What *is* green and hairy and goes up and down?
Duster A gooseberry in a lift. (*He roars with laughter*)

There is no reaction from the King

King Was it on a saucer?
Duster What?
King This gooseberry. Was it on a saucer?
Duster I don't know.
King Well, what a stupid joke. Most unhygienic — a gooseberry in contact with the floor of a lift. Ugh. Was it a washed gooseberry?
Duster I don't know. I didn't think it mattered.
King Didn't think it mattered? Of course it matters. Unwashed gooseberries give you collywobbles. It sound a most unhygienic joke. Make the next one cleaner. Remember where you are.
Duster Yes, your Majesty.
King (*muttering to himself*) Unwashed gooseberries on lift floors. Disgusting!
Duster Sorry, your Majesty.
King Fetch my dressing-gown. It's so embarrassing, wandering around in one's underwear, even if it is in one's own palace.

Duster One dressing-gown coming up, your Majesty.

Duster exits

King He seems harmless enough. I must have been wrong about him.

From off, there is a muffled scream and thud

Ah, Gadget's on his way. Hope he's all right on that ladder.

Measle enters disguised as Duster — in fact wearing Duster's outer garments. He carries the King's dressing-gown. It will be most effective if even the audience do not realize for a while what has happened

Measle (*imitating Duster*) Dressing-gown, your Majesty.

The King puts on his dressing-gown, helped by Measle

King Ah, thank you, Duster. I was just saying to myself, I hope Gadget will be safe on the roof.
Measle I'm sure he can take care of himself, your Majesty.
King Let's hope we can *all* take care of ourselves, eh? Don't want a spotty Court. I say, how do you think measles come?
Measle You catch them.
King Yes, but how do they start? How do they come in the first place?
Measle Well, your Majesty, perhaps there is a creature called Measle, who brings it by air — sort of slight, furry creature of a desperate character.
King (*roaring with laughter*) Ha, ha! Now that is a good joke, Duster. You're improving. Creatures called Measles. Ha, ha!

Measle swiftly pops a pill in the King's open mouth. The King gulps and swallows it

Measle No, not creatures called Measles. (*Throwing off his disguise*) A creature called Measle — ME!

The King screams with horror

King The pill, the pill?
Measle My signature, of course. You'll see spots soon!

Duster, in his underwear, reels in, recovering from being knocked out by Measle. Measle sees Duster and starts to run off. Duster blocks his path. The King gets up to help. They chase one another round

Eventually Measle escapes

The King and Duster are left bumping into each other, as the Lights fade to a Blackout

JANE EYRE
adapted by Willis Hall from the novel by Charlotte Brontë

Charlotte Brontë's story needs little introduction, and in this adaptation, a series of short scenes are linked by narration and movement. This extract effectively covers the period from Jane's initial interview with Mr Brocklehurst, her life at Lowood School and her acceptance as governess at Thornfield Hall. Here is a chance to use the acting area with simple settings, effects and properties.

Set: The drawing-room and driveway of Gateshead Hall, a classroom at Lowood School, Miss Temple's apartment, the Sick Room, Lowood School, outside St Stephen's Church, Lowood, Jane's Bedroom, Lowood School and finally Thornfield Hall.
The setting of these eight short scenes is as simple as possible, as the Narrators provide the link, and the characters move into the next scene. Period: mid Victorian.

Cast: M4 F7, 2M or F, 1 girl. Extras.
Jane Eyre, about 10 years old in the earlier scenes, 18 later. Mrs Reed, Jane's aunt by marriage, hard and domineering. Mr Brocklehurst, a clergyman, grim, stern; middle age. Bessie, a nursemaid, kindly. Groom at Gateshead Hall. Miss Temple, the school superintendent; 30. Helen Burns, a delicate pupil at Lowood, friend to Jane. Barbara, a maid. An orphan and school children. Narrators. Mrs Fairfax, the housekeeper at Thornfield Hall; elderly. Mr Naysmith, Miss Temple's bridegroom. Porter at Lowood. Adele Varens, a pretty girl; about 8.

Playing time: 28 minutes.

SCENE A

Mrs Reed and Mr Brocklehurst, a tall, harsh, prim man, enter in conversation. Mr Brocklehurst is carrying a book

Mrs Reed As I intimated in my letter, Mr Brocklehurst, the girl has neither the character nor the disposition I would wish. Should you admit her into Lowood School, I would be glad if the superintendent and teachers were requested to keep a strict eye on her.

Jane enters nervously

I was just telling Mr Brocklehurst, Jane, to instruct his staff to guard against your worst fault: a tendency to deceit. And I mention it too, in your hearing, that you may not attempt to impose on him or her.

Brocklehurst Her size is small. What is her age?

Mrs Reed Ten years.

Brocklehurst So much? (*He beckons Jane towards him with crooked forefinger*) Your name, little girl?

Jane Jane Eyre, sir.

Brocklehurst No sight so sad as that of a naughty child. Do you know where the wicked go after death?

Jane They go to hell.

Brocklehurst And what is hell, can you tell me that?

Jane A pit full of fire.

Brocklehurst And what must you do to avoid it?

Jane I must keep in good health and not die.

Brocklehurst How can you keep in good health? Children younger than you die daily. I buried a little child of five years old only a day or two since—a good little child, whose soul is now in heaven. It is feared that the same could not be said of you, were you to be summoned thence. (*To Mrs Reed*) Deceit is a sad fault in a child—a deceitful child is the next thing to an outright liar. She shall be watched, Mrs Reed. I will speak to Miss Temple and the teachers.

Mrs Reed I should wish her to be brought up in a manner suiting her prospects: to be useful, to be kept humble. As for the vacations, she will, with your permission, spend them always at the school.

Brocklehurst Your decisions are perfectly judicious, madam. Humility is a Christian grace. Little girl, here is a book entitled *The Child's Guide*.

He gives the book to Jane

Read it with prayer, especially that part containing "an account of the awfully sudden death of Martha Grantham, a naughty child addicted to falsehood". (*To Mrs Reed*) And now I must bid you good-morning.

Brocklehurst exits

Mrs Reed (*turning on Jane; angrily*) Go out of the room. Return to the nursery.

Jane I am not deceitful. If I were, I should say that I loved you, Aunt Reed. But I declare that I do not love you. I dislike you the worst of anybody in the world. And this book about the Liar, you may give it to your daughter, Georgina, for it is she who tells lies and not I!

Jane throws the book down on the floor at Mrs Reed's feet and storms out of the room as the Lights fade and come up immediately on two of the Narrators, standing at either end of the gallery

First Narrator Five o'clock had hardly struck on the morning of the nineteenth of January. I was already up and nearly dressed.

Second Narrator I was to leave Gateshead that day by coach which passed the lodge at six a.m.

First Narrator Bessie was the only person yet risen.

By which time, the Lights have come up on:

SCENE B

The Driveway, Gateshead Hall

It is a chill winter's morning before first light and we can hear the sound of impatient horses anxious to be off. The Groom puts down a lantern. Bessie hands him a small trunk and he takes it off to load on to the coach

Bessie picks up the lantern which the Groom has put down as Jane enters

Bessie Did you go in and bid Mrs Reed goodbye?

Jane Your missis, Bessie, has not been my friend—she has been my foe.

Bessie Don't say that, Miss Jane.

Jane What does it matter? I shall soon have another set of people to dread.

Bessie If you dread them, they'll dislike you.

Jane As you do, Bessie?

Bessie I don't dislike you, miss. Why, I am fonder of you than of the other children.

Jane You've never shown it.

Bessie And you're so glad to leave me?

Jane Not at all, Bessie. Just now I am rather sorry.

Bessie I dare say now if I were to ask you for a goodbye kiss, you wouldn't give it to me?

Jane I'll kiss you goodbye and welcome, Bessie.

They embrace, warmly

The Groom returns

Groom (*gently prising Jane loose*) The coach is waiting. Come on, Miss Eyre.

Jane Goodbye to Gateshead Hall.

Jane exits to join the coach

Bessie and the Groom watch her go

Groom How far is it?
Bessie Fifty miles.
Groom What a long way! I wonder Mrs Reed is not afraid to trust her so far alone.
Bessie She's a strange child. A lonely frightened little thing. (*She calls to the coach driver*) Be sure and take good care of her!

As we hear the coach rattle off along the drive, the Groom puts an arm around Bessie's waist which surprises but does not displease her. The Lights fade on the Driveway and come up on the gallery

First Narrator I remember but little of the journey here to Lowood Orphanage— except that we travelled from before first light until very late last night. Yesterday the fear of the unknown drove away my appetite.
Second Narrator This morning I was ravenous except the porridge that was given to us for breakfast was so burnt that not a single girl that I saw managed more than a spoonful—even a teacher said that it was "abominable stuff" and "shameful".

Over which, the Lights have come up on:

SCENE C

A classroom, Lowood School

Some half-dozen Girl Orphans (Jane is one of them) are standing behind child-size chairs. There is also a blackboard. Miss Temple, the school superintendent, aged thirty, wearing a "purple dress trimmed with black velvet and with a gold watch at her girdle" is in conversation with Mr Brocklehurst

Miss Temple I must be responsible for the circumstance, sir. The breakfast was so ill-prepared that the pupils could not possibly eat it. And I dare not let them remain fasting until dinner time.

Brocklehurst's reply is intended for the pupils as well as Miss Temple and he prowls around the class as he delivers it

Brocklehurst Madam, allow me an instant. You are aware that my plan in bringing up these girls is not to accustom them to habits of luxury and indulgence, but to render them hardy, patient, self-denying. Should any little accidental disappointment of the appetite occur, a brief address on those occasions would not be mistimed, wherein a judicious instructor would take the opportunity of referring to the sufferings of the primitive Christians; to the torments of martyrs; to the exhortations of Our Blessed Lord Himself, calling upon his disciples to take up their cross and follow Him; to His warnings that man shall not live by bread alone, but by every word that proceedeth out of the mouth of God; to His divine consolations, "If ye suffer hunger or thirst for My sake, happy are ye." Oh, madam, when you put bread and cheese, instead of burnt porridge, into these children's mouths, you may indeed feed their vile bodies—but you little think how you starve their immortal soul! Have them all sit down—except Helen Burns.

Miss Temple Sit down, girls.

They all sit—with the exception of a frail girl, Helen Burns. Helen's cough has drawn Brocklehurst's attention to her

Brocklehurst (*prowling the classroom*) Straighten up, Burns. Burns, you poke your chin out most unpleasantly. Draw it in. Burns, I insist on you holding up your head, you dirty, disagreeable girl.

Unintentionally, Jane drops her slate which crashes on the floor. Brocklehurst speaks without looking round

A careless girl. It is the new pupil, I perceive. I must not forget I have a word to say respecting her. Let the child who dropped her slate come forward.

As Jane crosses to the front of the class, Brocklehurst picks up the chair and places it for her to stand on. She does so

Miss Temple, children—you all see this girl? You observe that God has graciously given her the shape that he has given to all of us—who would think that the Evil One had already found a servant and an agent in her? It is my duty to warn you of this girl. Be on your guard against her. Shun her example. Avoid her company. Exclude her from your games. Shut her out of your conversations. Miss Temple, you will advise the staff to watch her carefully—to scrutinize her actions—to punish her body to save her soul—if, indeed, such salvation be possible. For this girl, this child, the native of a Christian land, worse than many a little heathen who says its prayers to Brahma and kneels before Juggernaut—this girl is—a liar! She has been sent here by her benefactress to be healed, even as the Jews of old sent their diseased to the troubled pool of——

Brocklehurst now pauses intimidatingly at an Orphan's side, inviting her to nominate the location—luckily, she is able to do so

Orphan (*nervously*) Bethesda.

Brocklehurst (*patting the Orphan on the head*) Bethesda—I beg of all of you, do not allow the waters to stagnate around her. (*To Miss Temple*) Let her stand half an hour longer on that chair—and let no-one speak to her during the remainder of the day. Good-morning, girls.

Girls Good-morning, Mr Brocklehurst.

Brocklehurst indicates that he wishes to speak in private to Miss Temple, and then moves to leave

Miss Temple Class monitors—you will see to it that there is no talking until the bell rings for prayers. You will then proceed, in single file, and join the rest of the school in the assembly hall.

Helen raises her hand

Yes, Helen?
Helen Should I collect the slates, Miss Temple?
Miss Temple You may.

Miss Temple follows Mr Brocklehurst out of the room

Helen collects in the slates and, as she passes Jane, she manages to give her a brief smile

As a handbell rings somewhere in the school, the Girls file out of the room. Helen, bringing up the rear, pauses long enough to smile again at Jane

Jane, who has stood with bowed head throughout her time in front of the class, is uplifted

Jane (*to the audience*) How much strength did I draw from that smile! How much friendship glowed in her eyes. It was as if a martyr, a hero, I had read about in books, had passed a slave or a prisoner and given out strength in passing. I was not alone any longer! I was suddenly borne up!

The Light fades, temporarily, on Jane, and comes up on the Narrators about the stage

First Narrator Ere the half-hour ended as five o'clock struck——
Second Narrator —it was deep dusk and I retired into a corner and sank down on the floor——
Third Narrator —overwhelmed with grief that seized me I sank with my face to the ground——
Fourth Narrator —here I lay crushed and trodden on—could I ever rise more?
Fifth Narrator Never! I thought how ardently I wished to die——
Sixth Narrator —whilst sobbing, someone approached me. Helen Burns was near.

The Lights come up on Jane who is huddled, sobbing, on the floor. Helen approaches her

Jane Helen, why do you stay with a girl whom everyone believes to be a liar? I know they despise me.

Helen Jane, you're mistaken. Probably not one in the school either despises or dislikes you.

Jane But if others don't love me, I'd rather die than live. I cannot bear to be solitary and hated, Helen. To gain some real affection from you or Miss Temple I would willingly submit to have the bone of my arm broken. Or to stand behind a kicking horse and let it dash its hoof at my chest.

Helen Hush, Jane.

Miss Temple enters

Miss Temple I came on purpose to find you, Miss Eyre. I want you in my room and as Helen Burns is with you, she may come too.

First Narrator We went. Following her guidance——

Second Narrator ——threading through intricate passages and mounting a staircase before we reached her apartment.

Jane and Helen move into the following scene, Miss Temple's apartment

The Lights fade and now come up on:

SCENE D

Miss Temple's apartment

Miss Temple's apartment is represented by three chairs and a side-table which is laid with tea and bread and butter for one. Miss Temple tugs an imaginary bell-rope

Miss Temple Is it all over? Have you cried your grief away?

Jane I am afraid that I shall never do that entirely.

Miss Temple Why?

Jane Because I have been wrongly accused—and you, ma'am, and everybody else will think me wicked.

Miss Temple We shall think you what you prove yourself to be, my child. If you obey the rules and continue to behave yourself, you will satisfy us.

Jane Shall I, Miss Temple?

Miss Temple You will.

A maid, Barbara, enters

Barbara, I am just about to have tea and have two visitors. Would you bring me extra cups and a little more bread and butter? There is not enough for three.

Barbara goes out

Be seated, girls.

They sit

How are you tonight, Helen? Have you coughed much today?
Helen Not quite so much, I think, ma'am.
Miss Temple And the pain in your chest?
Helen It is a little better.

Miss Temple crosses and takes Helen's pulse

Miss Temple You're both my guests tonight.

Barbara returns with a tray which holds two cups and saucers, which she places with the other tea-things

Where's the extra bread and butter?
Barbara Miss Temple, Mrs Harden says that she has already sent up the usual quantity.
Miss Temple Oh, very well. We must make it do, I suppose.

Barbara goes out

Fortunately, I have it in my power to supply deficiencies for this once. (*She takes a small package out of a drawer in the table and unwraps it*) I meant to give you both some of this fine seed-cake to take with you, but as there is so little bread and butter, you must have it now.

As Miss Temple serves the tea, the Lights fade

SCENE E

The Sick Room, Lowood School

Helen is in a small iron-bound bed covered with rough blankets. A Nurse is sitting in a chair at the end of the bed and is asleep. It is night, and there is one flickering candle on the floor. Jane tiptoes into the sick room

Jane Helen? Are you awake? Helen?
Helen (*close to death*) Can it be you, Jane? Why are you come here? It's past eleven o'clock—I heard the church clock strike some minutes since.
Jane They told me you were very ill. I couldn't sleep until I'd spoken to you.

Helen You came to say goodbye then? You are probably just in time.
Jane Are you going somewhere, Helen? Are you going home?

Helen coughs

Helen Yes. To my long home—my last home.
Jane No, no, Helen ...

Helen props herself up in bed

Helen I am very happy, Jane—and you must promise not to grieve for me when I am
dead. There is nothing to grieve about. We must all die one day. My mind is at rest.
I have no pain now. I am ready to go.
Jane But where are you going to, Helen? Do you know?
Helen I believe. I have faith, I am going to God.
Jane Where is God? What is God?
Helen He is our Maker, Jane, mine and yours. I believe both in His power and in His
goodness.
Jane You are sure then, Helen, that there is such a place as heaven?
Helen I am sure that there is a future state and I count the hours until I am summoned
there to meet Him face to face. He is my Father. He is my friend. I love Him and I
believe that He loves me. How comfortable I am! But that last fit of coughing has
tired me a little. Don't leave me, Jane. I like to have you near me.
Jane I am here, dear Helen. No-one shall take me away.
Helen Jane, your little feet are bare. Lie down and cover yourself with my quilt.

Jane gets into the bed

Are you warm, darling?
Jane Yes, Helen.
Helen Good-night, Jane.
Jane Good-night, Helen.

*They sleep. The Lights fade down and up into morning. The Nurse wakes, blows out
her candle and crosses to the bed. Helen is dead, one arm hangs lifeless. The Nurse
gently wakens Jane*

Nurse Miss Eyre. Wake up, Miss Eyre.
Jane Helen, wake up. Helen. Helen, don't leave me. Helen, come back!
Nurse Come on, miss. (*She gently helps Jane to her feet and moves her some paces
from the bed*) Stay there.

*The Nurse folds Helen's arms across her chest and then covers her face with the
blanket*

The Light fades up to day, the single tolling of a funeral bell changes into a happy pealing, as we go to:

SCENE F

Outside St Stephen's Church, Lowood

Eight years later

Where tragedy is turned into joy as Miss Temple enters on the arm of her new husband, Mr Naysmith. As the Girls chatter excitedly upstage with Mr Naysmith, Miss Temple moves downstage to meet Jane

Miss Temple Your kind thoughts, dearest Jane, mean more to me than those of any other person.

Jane They are heartfelt, Miss Temple—forgive me, Mrs Naysmith—of that, I promise you.

Miss Temple And what of you? Have you decided yet what's next, now that you are a woman? You could stay on at Lowood and continue teaching?

Jane Teaching, yes—but not at Lowood. Without you there, there is no place for me.

Miss Temple Then where? And how do you intend to find a position?

Jane I shall advertise.

Miss Temple Advertise?

Jane For a post as a private tutor: English, French, Drawing, Music—and in the *Yorkshire Herald*, where I have seen several such situations both advertised and sought for. You enclose the advertisement and the money to pay for it under a cover directed to the editor—I shall ask for answers, should there be any, to be addressed to me—I shall use my initials, J.E.—at the Post Office here in Lowood. Then, assuming that ...

Having been carried away by her own enthusiasm, Jane realizes that the bridegroom, Mr Naysmith, has approached and is holding out his hands to his bride. Jane kisses Miss Temple, impulsively

God bless you both and keep you very happy.

As the bride and groom go off, hand in hand, the Lights fade on the wedding scene and a spot comes up on Mrs Fairfax, an elderly lady in "widow's cap, black silk gown and snowy white muslin apron," who is standing on the gallery, reading a letter she has just penned

Mrs Fairfax If "J.E." who advertised in the *Yorkshire Herald* of last Thursday, possesses the acquirements mentioned—and if she is in a position to give satisfactory references as to character and competency——

Over which, the Lights come up on:

SCENE G

Jane's Bedroom, Lowood School

Where Jane is kneeling on the floor, packing her trunk, as Mrs Fairfax continues

Mrs Fairfax ... situation can be offered here where there is but one pupil, a little girl, under ten years of age, and where the salary is thirty pounds per annum. J.E. is requested to send references, name and address, and all particulars to the direction of Mrs Fairfax, Thornfield, near Millcote, West Yorkshire ...

As the Light fades on Mrs Fairfax, a Porter enters Jane's room

Porter There is someone called to see you, Miss Eyre.
Jane To see me? You're mistaken, surely?

Bessie enters

Bessie No, Miss Jane, there is no mistake.

She nods to the Porter who goes out

You've not forgotten me, I think?
Jane Bessie! But you are fortunate to have found me—one day later, Bessie, and I would have been gone from this place.
Bessie I knew that, miss, from the letter you wrote to Mrs Reed.
Jane Only because she is my legal guardian still, and I needed her permission to leave—but otherwise I have neither set eyes on her nor made contact with her these past eight years. You are at Gateshead Hall still?

Overcome at this reunion after all the years, Jane hugs Bessie

Bessie! Bessie!
Bessie I am married now to Robert, the groom whom you may remember? And we have two children, Bobby and Jane. When I heard missis say you were going to another part of the country, I thought I'd just set off and get a look at you, before you were quite out of my reach. You're not grown so very tall, Miss Jane, nor so very stout. I dare say they've not kept you too well at this place—but here you are—a teacher now—and a room all to yourself.

Jane Half a room Bessie. There is a Miss Gryce who takes History and Geography and Bible Studies and snores. But I shall have a room of my own at Thornfield Hall.

Jane feels that Bessie is looking at her with a critical eye

Oh, I am afraid you are disappointed in me, Bessie?

Bessie No, Miss Jane, not exactly. You are genteel enough. You look like a lady— and it is as much as I ever expected of you. You were no beauty as a child. I daresay you are clever though. You play the piano?

Jane A little.

Bessie And can draw and paint?

Jane Yes.

Bessie And you have learnt French?

Jane Yes, Bessie, I can both read it and speak it.

Bessie Oh, you are quite a lady, Miss Jane! You will get on whether your relations notice you or not—which brings me to another matter: have you heard anything from your father's kinsfolk, the Eyres? Missis said that they were poor and not worth speaking to—only one day, several months ago this was, a Mr Eyre came to the house and asked to see you. Mrs Reed told him you was away at school. He was that disappointed. He was sailing off to a foreign land the very next day and so could not arrange to see you. But I managed to pass a word with him and he gave me this to pass on to you. (*She produces a scrap of paper which she hands to Jane*) He said he was your father's brother—his address I believe it is. He said he would dearly like to hear from you.

Jane And I from him, Bessie.

Bessie Missis would scarcely give him the time of day—you know how short she can be with them she takes against.

Jane As well as anyone knows, Bessie.

The Porter returns

Jane nods at him

He carries out the trunk

But let's not dwell on Mrs Reed. We have such little time to spend together, I would rather talk of more pleasant matters. (*She puts on her bonnet, gloves and shawl*) Come, let us go out into the grounds until the carriage is ready and you shall tell me all about your children.

Bessie And I'm anxious to hear your news, Miss Jane. Missis let out that you'd secured a post as a governess?

Jane and Bessie move downstage as the Lights come up on:

Scene H

Thornfield Hall

Adele Varens, a pretty girl, about eight years old, whose waist-length hair and expensive Parisian clothes are in sharp contrast to the plain dresses of the orphan girls at Lowood School, is sitting on the floor, turning the pages of a book, as Jane continues talking to Bessie, downstage

Jane To a family by the name of Fairfax, Bessie, that lives at a Thornfield Hall, near Millcote, and with just one child that I shall have charge of — though what kind of folk they are, or what manner of place it is, or even what future lies in store for me, I know not — except that I hope with all my heart that my time at Thornfield may serve to provide me with happier memories than many of those I shall take with me from Lowood.

THE LION, THE WITCH AND THE WARDROBE
by C.S. Lewis, adapted by Glyn Robbins

An adaptation of the novel, this dramatic scene develops to the climax of the death of Aslan, the Lion. The setting is the Land of Narnia, through the wardrobe, where the four children: Peter, Susan, Edmund and Lucy have their adventures. The White Witch, who represents the forces of evil, has captured Edmund. In the fight between her Dwarf and Aslan's guards, the Leopards, the Witch escapes, and Edmund is rescued and brought to Aslan. The Lion represents all that is good. There is much opportunity for originality in direction, with challenging effects to create.

Set: The Stone Table and Aslan's Pavilion in the Land of Narnia in Spring.

Cast: M6 F2, 2 boys 2 girls. Extras.
Peter, Edmund, Lucy and Susan, the children who have stepped into the wardrobe and have adventures in the Land of Narnia. Aslan, the Lion. Mr and Mrs Beaver, two friendly beavers. The White Witch, the evil one. The Dwarf, her slave. Leopard 1 and Leopard 2, guards to Aslan. Maugrim, a wolf. The Uglies.

Playing time: 14 minutes.

The Leopards enter with Edmund. Aslan enters. Aslan approaches a very shame-faced Edmund

Edmund I'm sorry, Aslan.

Aslan roars. He exits into the pavilion with his arm around Edmund. The Leopards follow

Lucy and Mrs Beaver enter, followed by Mr Beaver

Lucy Is it true? Is it true?
Mrs Beaver It must be, dearie. We heard it from one of the leopards himself.
Mr Beaver First paw, as it were.

Susan and Peter enter

Susan Have you heard? Isn't it wonderful?
Lucy It is true, then.
Peter Yes. They rescued Edmund last night. But unfortunately in all the confusion the Witch got away. Still, they think she was badly hurt, so she can't have got far.
Susan Where's Edmund now?
Lucy And how is he?
Peter He's fine. A bit shaken. And he's had a great fright. But Aslan's talking with him now.

Aslan enters with Edmund

Aslan Here is your brother, at last. He has something to say to you. There is no need now to talk to him about what is past.

Edmund moves towards the others. Lucy goes to him and embraces him

Lucy Oh, Edmund.

Lucy leads Edmund to join the other children and the Beavers. All is forgiven

Leopard 1 enters

Leopard 1 Sire, a messenger has arrived from the enemy.
Aslan Let the messenger approach.

Leopard 1 beckons

The Dwarf enters escorted by Leopard 2

What is your message, Son of Earth?
Dwarf Greetings, Aslan. The Queen of Narnia ...
Mr Beaver Queen of Narnia, indeed. She's got a cheek!
Aslan Peace, Beaver. All names and titles will soon be restored to their rightful owners.
Dwarf The Queen of ... that is, the Empress of the Lone Islands desires a safe conduct, that she may come and speak with you on a matter which is as much to your advantage as to hers.
Aslan Son of Earth, tell your mistress that I grant her safe conduct on the condition that she leaves her magic wand behind her at the Great Oak Tree.
Dwarf I am already empowered to agree that condition. Therefore I will return and bring her here.

Aslan Leopards, go with him and ensure the condition is carried out.

The Leopards exit with the Dwarf

Lucy (*whispering*) But suppose she changes the leopards to stone too.
Mrs Beaver Mighty Aslan wouldn't send them if it weren't all right.
Lucy I suppose not.
Susan I wonder if she really is badly hurt?

The sky darkens and a wind howls

The White Witch enters, unhurt

White Witch (*pointing at Edmund*) You have a traitor there, Aslan.
Aslan His offence was not against you, Witch.
White Witch Have you forgotten the Deep Magic?
Aslan Let us say I have forgotten it. Tell us all of this "Deep Magic".
White Witch Tell you? Tell you what is written in letters as deep as a spearhead is long on the Stone Table that stands there, beside us? You know very well that every traitor belongs to me as my lawful prey, and that for every treachery, I have a right to kill. (*Pointing at Edmund*) That human creature, that Son of Adam, is mine. His life is forfeit to me. His blood is my property.
Peter (*drawing his sword in challenge to the Witch*) Come and take it then!
White Witch (*disarming Peter with her gaze and laughing*) Little fool! Do you really think that you can rob me of my rights by mere force? Your Master knows the Deep Magic better than that. Unless I have the blood, as the Law says, all Narnia will be overwhelmed and perish in fire and water.
Aslan I do not deny it.
Lucy Oh, Aslan, can't we—can't we do something about the Deep Magic? Isn't there some spell you can work against it?
Aslan (*roaring*) Work against the Emperor's Deep Magic? Do not ever suggest that again, Daughter of Eve. Fall back all of you. I would talk with the White Witch alone.

Everybody falls back as the Lights dim around Aslan and the Witch who come together in silent debate and argument. An enormous battle of wills is going on. A resolution is reached. The White Witch laughs

White Witch But, Aslan, how do I know your promise will be kept?

In reply, Aslan throws back his head and gives a deafening roar

The Witch hastily exits

Aslan You must all listen, now. We have settled the matter. The Witch has renounced her right to your brother's blood.

Everyone cheers

Peter, we must now discuss the battle.

Mrs Beaver (*taking Aslan's hint*) You must be worn out, dears. Come along now. It's almost Moon-up and time for all good folk to be tucked up tight and safe in bed. Come on.

Mrs Beaver ushers everyone out through the pavilion, leaving Aslan and Peter alone

The Lights dim

Aslan As soon as the Witch has finished her business in these parts, she and her crew will almost certainly fall back to her castle and prepare for a siege. Now, let's look at the map. You can try to cut them off and fight them in the woods, or you can attack the Witch's castle. My advice to you is——

Peter But Aslan, you will be there yourself.

Aslan I can give you no promise of that. Now, watch closely.

Aslan and Peter converse quietly, looking at the map of Narnia

Unseen by them, Lucy enters, followed by Susan

Susan You must try to get some sleep. It'll do you good.

Lucy I couldn't sleep. I have the most horrible feeling.

Susan Are you ill?

Lucy No. I just feel as if something was hanging over us. Something awful. Like a big, black storm.

Susan It must be because it's so dark.

Peter But Aslan, wouldn't it be better to camp on the far side? She might try a night attack.

Aslan (*deep in thought*) Eh? What did you say, Peter?

Peter Camp on the far side? Possible night attack?

Aslan (*dully*) No, no. She won't attack tonight. (*More brightly*) But that, Peter, is just how a soldier should think. Well done. You know enough now to lead the animals in order of battle.

Peter But you will be there, won't you?

Aslan We shall see. But anyway, a wise captain makes sure his second-in-command is well-informed. You must leave me now. Good-night, Peter.

Peter Good-night, Aslan.

Peter exits

Susan Do you still feel strange?
Lucy Yes. It's something awful about Aslan. Something really dreadful.
Susan Something dreadful he is going to do? Or something dreadful that is going to happen to him?
Lucy I don't know. I don't know. Just something dreadful.
Susan There's been something wrong with him all afternoon. Ever since he met the Witch.
Lucy Is he hurt do you think? Perhaps I should use my little bottle of fireflower juice?
Susan No, he's not exactly hurt. Just extremely worried about something.
Lucy Let's go to him.

They approach Aslan

Aslan!
Aslan Hush, child. You should be asleep, Lucy. You too, Susan.
Susan Lucy couldn't sleep. Nor could I. We were worried about you. Is there anything we can do? Can we stay with you? Keep you company?
Aslan I would be glad of company tonight. So, please stay—as long as you promise to leave me immediately, when I tell you.
Lucy Aslan, dear Aslan, what's wrong? Can't you tell us?
Susan Are you ill? Are you hurt?
Lucy Can I give you some of my fireflower juice?
Aslan No, thank you, Lucy. No. I'm not hurt. Nor ill, Susan. Just a little sad and lonely. Put your hands on my mane so that I can feel that you both are with me and let us stand together like this for a time.

The girls obey. The tranquillity is broken by the howl of a wolf

Children, children, now you must go. Whatever happens, do not let yourselves be seen.

Another howl

Thank you for being with me. Now go!

Susan and Lucy pretend to leave Aslan, but hide instead. Aslan climbs on to the Stone Table and remains there on all fours. The Lights dim further and a wind howls, causing the drapes to billow

Gradually, the Uglies, etc., enter one by one and to the accompaniment of shrieks, howls etc. The Dwarf and Maugrim enter and finally, when all are assembled, the White Witch enters in a white light

White Witch (*seeing Aslan*) Aslan! The fool! The fool is here! Bind him fast!

The Dwarf and Maugrim approach Aslan fearfully, with a rope

Bind him, I say!

Discovering that Aslan makes no resistance, they rush at him and bind him. Other Uglies join in with taunts and jibes

Let him first be shaved!

A roar of laughter and the Dwarf produces an evil-looking pair of shears and cuts off Aslan's mane

Maugrim Why, he's only a great big cat after all!
Dwarf A bare-cat!
Maugrim Is that what we've all been afraid of?
Dwarf Here, Pussy, Pussy. Here, Pussy, Pussy!

Another roar of laughter

Maugrim And how many mice have you caught today, little Cattikins?
Dwarf How would you like a nice big saucer of milk, Pussums?

More laughter

White Witch Muzzle him!

Maugrim and other animals react violently crying "What?"

Muzzle him! NOW!

They obey. The White Witch draws her dagger

And who has won now, Aslan? Fool! Did you think by all this sacrifice that you would save the human traitor? Now I will kill you instead of him and appease the Deep Magic. But when you are dead what is there to stop me from killing him as well? You see you have not saved his life, you have lost your own, and you have given me Narnia forever! In that knowledge Aslan, despair and die! (*She raises her dagger and stabs Aslan*)

The Uglies, Dwarf and Maugrim give a shout of triumph. They all exit with much cacophony bearing the Witch high, leaving Aslan dead on the Stone Table

Lucy and Susan come out of hiding in floods of tears

Lucy The brutes! The cowards!

The wind stops

Susan How could they do that to Aslan? Poor, poor Aslan! Poor, poor Narnia!
Lucy What will become of us all now?

They both approach the Stone Table

   Is he really dead?
Susan Yes, Lucy. I'm afraid he really is dead.
Lucy That awful muzzle. Can we take it off?
Susan Of course we can.

They remove it

Lucy Could we untie him as well?
Susan Of course.

They try, but fail

Lucy I'm so cold, my fingers won't work.
Susan Come on. Let's try again.
Lucy Ugh! Look at that!
Susan How horrible! Horrible little mice crawling all over him.
Lucy How could they? How could they?
Susan Wait! Can you see what they're doing?
Lucy Yes, I can. They're nibbling at the ropes.
Susan They are trying to untie him, too! Poor little mice. They think it will help.

The girls attempt to free the ropes again and succeed. A bird chuckles and startles them. Dawn is coming

Lucy What was that?
Susan It must be a bird waking up. It's so cold. Let's walk about to keep warm. It'll
   soon be morning.

They do. Lucy's attention is caught by something in the sky

Lucy Susan, just look at that star! It's like a diamond!

Susan moves to Lucy and together they admire the heavens. The sky darkens and goes black. There is a huge rumbling sound followed by a deafening cracking sound as the Stone Table splits in two, with a flash and smoke

Susan What was that?
Lucy I'm afraid.
Susan Something awful is happening.
Lucy They're doing something worse to him.

Finally the noise abates and light returns. The crouching, terrified girls pluck up courage to look around. Aslan has disappeared

Susan What's happened? Where's he gone?
Lucy They've taken him.
Susan What can it mean? Is it more of that awful "Deep Magic"?

Aslan appears shrouded in a golden light

Lucy!
Both Aslan!
Lucy But you're dead? Are you a ghost?
Aslan No.
Susan What does it all mean?
Aslan It means that although the White Witch knew the Deep Magic well enough, her knowledge only goes back as far as the dawn of time. If she could have looked back a little further, into the stillness and darkness of before time began, she would have known there is a deeper, older, better, magic. She would have known of a different spell, another incantation. She would have known that when a willing victim died in the place of a traitor, the Stone Table would crack, and Death itself would work backwards.
Susan Which all means that you are alive.
Lucy You're really, really alive?
Aslan Yes, I am.
Lucy Not a ghost?
Aslan Do I look like one? Pinch me!

Both girls run to him and pinch him

Ouch! Not that hard. I'm still a little weak. But I feel my strength coming back in leaps and bounds.

Aslan proceeds to leap and bound chased by a delighted Lucy and Susan

A LITTLE PRINCESS
adapted by Michael Wild
from the original by Frances Hodgson Burnett

Many will have read the much-loved novel set at the turn of the century, and will realize the importance of this crucial birthday party scene, when Sara Crewe's life will change so dramatically. The formal style is challenging to capture with precision and poise, and there is a chance to be imaginative with the staging of these three scenes, with Becky linking the two short episodes at the end.

Set: Miss Minchin's Academy — three areas, the last being the attic room. Period: late nineteenth century.

Cast: M2 F3. 8 girls.
Sara Crewe. Miss Minchin, Principal of the Academy. Miss Amelia, her sister. Lavinia, Lottie, Jessie and Ermengarde, schoolgirls. Becky, a scullery-maid. 1st, 2nd and 3rd girl pupils. A French maid. James, the footman. Mr Barrow, a solicitor.

Playing time: 16 minutes.

SCENE A

The Lights come up to reveal Miss Amelia standing in front of the Girls who are grouped formally. She is conducting in a rather over-flowery fashion. Everybody is wearing her best party frock—some of them looking very uncomfortable indeed

Miss Amelia Now, girls, we'll try that just once again. Have you got the note? Not too loudly, she'll be down in a minute, and we don't want her to hear. (*Singing*) Ah ...
Lavinia } (*together*) { Urrrrr ...
Ermengarde } (*together*) { Ahhhhh ...
Lottie (*making a dreadful noise*) Ahhhhhooooh.

Amelia winces but carries bravely on. She calls for "Harmony!" The Girls sing a chord in three-part harmony, rather badly, then launch into "Happy Birthday"

Sara comes in with Miss Minchin and the French Maid

Ermengarde Here's my present. (*She kisses Sara*)
Lottie Here's my present. (*She hugs Sara*)
First Girl Here is mine—
Second Girl And mine—
Third Girl And mine ...

They nearly fight to get to Sara

All Happy birthday to you. (*They break into excited chatter and laughter*)

James, the footman, enters with a large box. After a moment Becky creeps in with her coal-box and a small parcel

More excitement as James enters

Miss Minchin Silence, young ladies.

The noise stops

This is not an ordinary occasion. I do not desire that it should be treated as one. James, place that box upon the table and remove the lid. Ermengarde, will you stop twitching!

There is a crash as Becky drops the coal-box

Rebecca, you forget yourself. It is not your place to look at the young ladies. Put your box down. You may leave us.

Lavinia and Jessie titter as Becky creeps by them, trying to see into the box

Sara (*suddenly*) If you please, Miss Minchin, mayn't Becky stay?
Miss Minchin (*aghast*) Becky! My dearest Sara—Becky is the scullery-maid.
Sara I want her because I know she will like to see the presents. She is a little girl too, you know.

More titters from Lavinia

Miss Minchin My dear Sara, Becky is the scullery-maid. Scullery-maids—er—are not little girls.
Sara But Becky is. Miss Minchin—please let her stay—because it is my birthday.
Miss Minchin As you ask it as a birthday favour, she may stay. Rebecca, go and stand there—not too near the young ladies.
Becky Oh, thank you, Miss Minchin. (*To Sara*) Thank you, miss. I'm that grateful, miss—and oh, miss ...

Miss Minchin clears her throat to speak

Amelia Hush!

Becky (*whispering*) Happy birthday, miss. It's a pin-cushion. (*She hands her parcel to Sara.*) It isn't very special, 'cos I made it myself

Sara (*hugging Becky*) Ohhh! (*She gasps*) Oh yes, it is, Becky. It's really special—'cos you made it yourself.

The doorbell rings

Miss Minchin Answer the door, James.

James exits

Miss Minchin and the girls speak the following together

Miss Minchin	Girls
And now, young ladies	Miss Minchin's Academy
I've something to say to you	Miss Minchin's Academy
Concerning Sara Crewe	This bloomin' old place
You've most of you	We're sent here at seven
Had birthdays before	And told we're in heaven
But this is special	Who fools who?

Amelia That's true

Miss Minchin
When she is older
She will be an heiress

Amelia Which should make us all feel   And won't Miss Minchin be glad.
glad.

Miss Minchin pats Sara's head. Sara shivers

Miss Minchin
Who knows, she may
    share that
Fortune with others   **Girls**

Amelia With others —   With others
With others —   With others
                                     She knows she better well had
                                     Meaning!

Miss Minchin mimes speaking

                                     Miss Minchin's Academy
                                     Miss Minchin's Academy

Miss Minchin (*aloud*)
  She's made our Academy Blue.   Glue, glue, glue
  I hope you will join me in thanking
Amelia   In thanking
Miss Minchin   In thanking
  Yes, gratefully thanking   **Lavinia** I'd give her a spanking.
  Thanking
  Thanking Sara Crewe.
Amelia One, two, three ...
All Thank you, Miss Sara. (*They cheer*)

James enters

James A Mr Barrow has called to see you, ma'am. Shall I ask him to come in?

Miss Minchin waves a hand of assent

James exits

Amelia Captain Crewe's solicitor—how convenient!
Miss Minchin Hush, Amelia. Now, Sara, your father's lawyer wishes to see me, but the party will not be curtailed. As refreshments are laid in the parlour, will you kindly lead the way?
Amelia And you, Becky, will go back to your work.

Amelia turns to Miss Minchin, and at this moment Becky slips under the table, and is hidden by the cloth

The Girls file out, talking quietly

What a strange hour to call.
Miss Minchin Amelia, you talk too much. You will accompany the girls. This may be private business.
Amelia The diamond mines, you think—a bequest?
Miss Minchin It may be a little thank-you for all we have done—who knows? *Wait and see!*

Amelia scuttles off. James and Mr Barrow, the solicitor, enter. James exits

(*Taking his hand*) Pray be seated, Mr Barrow.
Barrow (*eyeing the presents*) All from the father, I suppose? (*Picking up a doll*) A hundred pounds, at least. All expensive material, and made at a Parisian modiste's. He spent money lavishly enough, that young man.
Miss Minchin I beg your pardon, Mr Barrow, I do not understand.

Barrow Birthday presents like these—to a child eleven years old! Mad extravagance, I call it.

Miss Minchin Captain Crewe is a man of fortune. The diamond mines alone ...

Barrow Diamond mines! There are none! Never were!

Miss Minchin No diamond mines? No diamond mines ... ?

Barrow Diamond mines spell ruin, madam, oftener than they spell wealth, especially if you're in the hands of a friend—and you're not much of a business man yourself. The late Captain Crewe ...

Miss Minchin The *late* Captain Crewe? The late ... You don't come to tell me that Captain Crewe ...

Barrow Is dead, ma'am. Jungle fever and business troubles combined—too much for him. The one was bad enough, the other finished him off. Died delirious, and raving about his little girl—and didn't leave a penny.

Miss Minchin Do you mean to tell me that he left nothing? That the child is a beggar—and left on my hands?

Barrow Right both times, ma'am. She hasn't a relation in the world, that we know of.

Miss Minchin But this is monstrous! She is in my sitting-room at this very moment, dressed in silk and gauze and lace petticoats, giving a party—at my expense! I paid the bill for that ridiculous doll and her ridiculous fantastic wardrobe. The child was to have everything she wanted. She has a carriage and a pony and a maid, and I have paid for them all since the last cheque came.

Barrow Well, you had better not pay for anything more, madam. She hasn't a brass farthing to call her own—and Barrow and Skipworth are not responsible. Very sorry, of course ...

Miss Minchin If you think she is to be foisted off on me you are mistaken. I have been robbed and cheated. I will turn her out into the streets.

Barrow I wouldn't do that, ma'am. It wouldn't look well for the—ahem—establishment. Pupil bundled out penniless and without friends. Better keep her and make use of her as she grows older.

Miss Minchin I'll make some good use.

Barrow Good-morning, now, to you.

Barrow exits

Miss Minchin rings a bell

Amelia comes scurrying in

Amelia What is the matter, sister dear?

Miss Minchin Tell that Sara Crewe to come here. Find her an old black frock at once. Don't just stand there, you stupid dunce. (*Screaming*) Captain Crewe is *dead*!

Amelia Dead!

Miss Minchin And she's no mother — that dear little baba whom I'd like to strangle and with her bills stuff her— *for never a penny I'll see*! Send little Sara, that dear little Sara, that spoilt, extravagant, hateful, penniless, ugly Princess Sara — (*screaming*) — send her at once to me!

Amelia rushes out

Becky sniffs, under the table

What is that?

Another sniff. Miss Minchin raises the cloth

How dare you! How *dare* you! Come out immediately.

Becky crawls out, petrified

Becky Oh, if you please, mum, I didn't 'ear nothin'. Mum, poor miss Sara. (*She sobs*) What will become of 'er?
Miss Minchin That is nothing to you. Leave the room this instant or you'll leave your place.
Becky Let me wait on 'er, mum—after I've done me pots and kettles. It's just like the stories, mum, just like the stories ...
Miss Minchin What stories? (*Shaking her*) What stories do you mean?
Becky Them poor princesses, mum—jest like Miss Sara—them that was driven out into the world ...

Becky runs off, sobbing. Amelia enters

Miss Minchin Is she coming? I don't want any crying, or unpleasant scenes.
Amelia Sister, she is the strangest child I ever saw. She has actually made no fuss at all. When I told her what had happened she just stood quite still and looked at me without making a sound. It made me feel quite queer not to be answered. Her eyes just got bigger and bigger and she went quite pale—but she didn't say a word.

There is a knock on the door

Miss Minchin Hush, here she is. Go now.

Amelia exits. Sara enters. She carries Emily and now wears an old, black, outgrown dress

Put down your doll. What do you mean by bringing her here?

Sara No! I will not put her down. She is all I have. My papa gave her to me.

Miss Minchin You will have no time for dolls in the future. Everything is very different now. Miss Amelia has explained matters to you?

Sara Yes. My papa is dead. He left me no money. I am quite poor.

Miss Minchin You are a beggar. You have no relations and no home—and no-one at all to take care of you.

Sara stares at her

What are you staring at? Are you so stupid that you cannot understand?

Sara I understand—I understand ...

Miss Minchin That *doll*—that ridiculous doll. I actually paid the bill for her. Everything you own is *mine*!

Sara Please take it away from me, then. I do not want it.

Miss Minchin Don't speak to me in that proud, arrogant way. You are like Becky now—you must work for your living. If I keep you here on charity you'll be made to lend a hand.

Sara Can I work? Oh, I can teach—the little ones like me, I know ...

Miss Minchin Don't talk nonsense about people liking you. You will run errands and help in the kitchen as well as in the schoolroom. If you don't please me you will be sent away. Remember that. Now ...

Sara Yes, Miss Minchin?

Miss Minchin Now—*go*!

Sara starts to go

Stop! Don't you intend to thank me?

Sara What for?

Miss Minchin For my kindness to you—for my kindness in giving you a home?

Sara You are not kind—you are *not* kind—and this is *not* a home ...

Sara runs off

Miss Minchin Well!

The Lights fade to a Black-out

SCENE B

The Lights come up on Becky and Amelia

Becky If you please, mum, Miss Amelia—where is Miss Sara? She is not in her room.

Amelia That is not her room any longer—I'm afraid.

Becky Not her room? Where is it, then?
Amelia In the attic next to you. That's where you'll find her. (*She turns away*)
Becky In the attic—oh, no, they can't do that. Miss Sara—Miss Sara ...

The Lights fade and come up on Sara with Emily in the attic

SCENE C

Becky taps on the door

Becky Oh miss—might I—would you allow me—just to come in?

Sara tries to smile, and holds out her hand

Sara Oh Becky, I told you we were just the same—just two little girls. You see how true it is. There's no difference now—I'm not a princess any more.
Becky Oh yes, miss, you are. Whatever happens to you—whatsoever—you'd be a princess all the same—and nothin' couldn't make you nothin' different ...

Sara smiles at Becky as the Lights fade

LORDS OF CREATION
by John Wiles

This folk-tale was written for a large cast, but the number and setting are flexible. Each creature must stand trial before the god, Tangaroa, to prove that he is worth saving and deserves to survive. It is Moja, the Lion's turn. There is much opportunity to present this scene with originality and effect. In the original production the cast were encouraged to make their own Oriental music with the aid of finger xylophones, gongs of various sizes and bells.

Set: A jungle clearing where a Court of Law has been arranged. The location should be South-East Asia.

Cast: 22 characters. Extras.
Tangaroa, the god in Oriental robes. Four Wise Ones, a panel of experts. Chamberlain, elaborately dressed, with staff. Storyteller. Recorder. Five Clerks. Moja, the lion. Lioness, his mate. Three Cubs. 1st Assistant. Stump Tooth, Moja's aged deputy. Jackal. Devil-lion. Drummers. Dancers, boys and girls with gongs, finger-bells or wooden clackers. Spectators.

Playing time: 15 minutes.

Storyteller The hearings are about to begin.

The Lights begin to narrow down until only the central area is lit. The Court is arranged with the Wise Ones taking their places on either side of Tangaroa and the Chamberlain's staff preparing their lists. One has the task of keeping the records by chiselling marks on a stone. Not surprisingly events always happen too fast for him

Recorder (*the stone-cutter*) What's the date?
3rd Clerk The twenty-first day after the Spring moon.
Recorder Thank you. (*He starts to chip at the stone*)
Chamberlain First candidate for survival — the lion!
1st Clerk The lion!
2nd Clerk The lion!
3rd Clerk (*sleepily*) Oh, not him again. The lion! Ho-hum ...

4th Clerk The lion!
Recorder How do you spell that?

4th Clerk shows him

5th Clerk The lion!
Storyteller (*to the audience*) We love ritual, you see.

The cry of "The lion!" is carried back into the wings

> *The Lion's party enter carrying their masks under their arms in the manner of warriors. They bow to the Court, don their masks, and take up their ritualistic starting positions. The music starts—gongs and bells. The Lions' Dance is one of catlike movements, stealthy but strong. They prowl ... pounce ... stretch ... wash their faces with their paws ... rear proudly ... sleep deeply ... wake instantly*

The spectators sway in time to the rhythm and make polite comments of appreciation. At the end of the dance, the music stops, the dancers hold their positions, and Moja steps forward. He tosses his mane proudly and flails with his paws

Moja I am Lion!
Spectators (*separately*) Yes, you can see that ... isn't he handsome ... I hope he's not too fierce ... *etc.*
Lioness (*rather bored*) I'm his mate.
Moja I am the King of the Beasts.
Lioness I'm his female.
Moja I strike terror into all who behold me.
Lioness Except me. I hunt for him, kill for him, bear his cubs and look after the family.
Cubs (*squeaky*) We're the family! (*They try to walk and fall over*)

The Lioness hauls them to their feet

Lioness The sooner you learn to walk the better.
Moja My story concerns Devil-beast, the greatest lion of them all. And how I defeated him.

Murmurs of excitement from the spectators

Lioness (*to the cubs*) Take your positions, and don't fall over.

Moja waves an imperious paw at the Storyteller's 1st Assistant

Moja Begin.

1st Assistant Very well. In the country of the Serengeti near the place known as Mamoto in the land of the two-leggeds called the Baganda, there lived a whole colony of lions ruled over by the King Moja.

The Lights come up very hot and dry

Moja I am Moja. It means Number One. I am King Number One of all the lions of the Serengeti. All who hear my roar, tremble!
Lioness Except me.
1st Assistant More than one hundred square miles belonged to this Moja. While his female hunted and protected the cubs, he patrolled his kingdom ceaselessly in the company of Stump Tooth, his aged deputy, to keep out intruders.

Moja and Stump Tooth prowl. The Lioness moves between the cubs, always watching, always expecting trouble. Moja and his friend reach a high point and there settle to survey the landscape and snuffle at the dust

Moja I tell you, Stump Tooth, I often wonder if in the whole universe of lions, I am not the greatest of them all.

Stump Tooth gives a non-commital grunt

Who else has a kingdom so wide, so long and so full of Thompson gazelles to please his stomach!

Stump Tooth gives another low growl

Well, speak up. Don't just lie there clearing your throat.
1st Assistant Now Stump Tooth was no fool. He didn't want to contradict Moja, you see, but he had heard, well, he had heard—well, you'll hear what he had heard.
Stump Tooth I think you're right to be proud, Moja. Your kingdom certainly is a glory to behold. Nevertheless, well ...
Moja (*sharply*) Nevertheless, what? Speak up!
Stump Tooth I have heard that over to the East there does live a beast so powerful, so menacing that when he shakes his mane the whole earth grows dark. And as for his roar ...
Moja What about his roar? Is it more terrible than mine?
Stump Tooth Well, they do say that when he shouts, the trees sway, the corn bows down and bolts of light come from the sky.
Moja Impossible. The lion who can make trees dance has never been invented, although I dare say I come pretty close to it.
Stump Tooth Well ... if you say so ...

Moja Of course I say so. Anyway, show me his face. Can any face be as handsome as mine?

Stump Tooth (*worried*) Nobody's seen his face, that's half the trouble. For whenever he appears, the sky is so full of streaks of light, you can't see anything else.

Moja (*impressed*) Simba ...

Stump Tooth As for his claws, they do tell how one swipe is enough to flatten all the grasslands between here and the Salt Water Hole, and you know how far off that is. (*He goes on talking in mime*)

1st Assistant And the more Stump Tooth went on speaking, the more impressed Moja became. Was there ever such a threat to his kingdom, he thought.

Moja I tell you, Stump Tooth, there is only one thing to do. You must seek out this devil and kill him.

Stump Tooth I? Not on your life.

Moja Why not? You're my deputy, the Number One of the Number One, are you not?

Stump Tooth But this is no job for a deputy! If anybody's going to challenge the monster, it ought to be you.

Moja Rubbish. It's below my dignity.

1st Assistant But in his heart, Moja knew his friend was right.

Moja (*aside*) Oh, Simba, I'm afraid. What Stump Tooth has said is the truth. It certainly is my task to challenge the outsider, but what can I do? Inside I am a very small lion, although the sweep of my tail is enough to put all the animals of my kingdom to flight.

1st Assistant And while Moja lay there digesting this terrible news, and Stump Tooth kept glancing over his shoulder in case the Devil-lion had crept up on them unnoticed, the sun bounced gently in the sky and then went down the hill in search of its blanket.

The Lights go to night

Meanwhile, back at the home-cave. (*Nervously to Moja*) We haven't done this bit.

Moja Just get on.

1st Assistant Back at the home-cave ...

1st Cub I'm hungry.

2nd Cub So am I.

3rd Cub Me too, me too!

1st Assistant I think that's right.

Lioness (*no nonsense*) Be quiet! Can't you see I'm just going out to find some food. And while I'm gone, don't take any chances. Lie very still and don't dare go outside. And don't forget to wash your feet. Remember what they say, a lion who doesn't wash his paws before going to sleep, lies down with the devil.

1st Cub I think it's a stupid expression. What's it mean, anyway?

Lioness It doesn't matter what it means, just remember it. Well, I'm off ...

2nd Cub Can we have buffalo tonight?

3rd Cub Or a nice mongoose?
Lioness You'll have what you're given and no nonsense. (*She goes*)

The cubs watch her go and then grow restless

1st Assistant But things didn't work out like that. The eldest cub who, as you've
   seen, was something of a teenage rebel, hardly waited for his mother to go, before
   he stuck his nose out of the cave. This attracted the attention of a Back-Striped
   Jackal who happened to be nosing about, and——

The Jackal slips into the cave

   —within a trice the cubs were dead. The youngest got as far as thinking, "perhaps
   we ought to have washed our paws after all", but the oldest knew it was his fault
   for sticking his nose outside the cave ... anyway it was soon over and when they
   opened their eyes again, they were in Simba-heaven which is a place very like this,
   only without any of the worries.

The Jackal eats his fill and then goes

   Meanwhile their mother was continuing to hunt. Torn between a wart hog, a Masai
   giraffe and a red duiker, she was trying to make up her mind when she was charged
   by a black rhinoceros and before she knew it, she was dead——

The fight is enacted as described

   —and had joined her children in Simba-heaven.
Lioness (*sitting up*) What are you all doing here?
3rd Cub We didn't listen to you, Mother.
Lioness Let that be a lesson to you.

They all lie down again

Storyteller You'll notice nobody thought to ask the mother what *she'd* learnt. But
   that's the privilege of mothers anywhere ...
1st Assistant Came the dawn ...

The Lights stay down

   Came the dawn ... came the dawn ...
Storyteller I think it's meant to be like this.
1st Assistant (*glancing at her scroll*) Ah, yes. Came the dawn, but instead of a
   lessening of the dark, the stars remained covered. Moja, who had spent the night
   travelling back to the home-cave with Stump Tooth, glanced up at the sky.

Moja I think we're in for a storm.
Stump Tooth (*nervously*) What if they're not clouds, but the flying mane of the Devil-beast?
Moja Nonsense, I'd recognize cumulo-nimbus anywhere.

A distant growl of thunder

Stump Tooth (*in a panic*) No, no, listen to that. I tell you that's his roar.
Moja Rubbish. Have you gone *bata*?
1st Assistant Bats.
Moja That's the voice of the rain-god.
Stump Tooth No, no, it's the growl of the Devil-lion.
Moja Are you sure? I could have sworn——

A giant crack of thunder, lightning and the sound of rain

Stump Tooth It is he, it is he!
Moja Oh, Simba, and I thought it was just the rain-god.

The thunder and rain continue. Moja and Stump Tooth take to their heels, seeking shelter. Moja stumbles over the body of the Lioness

(*Shouting over the storm*) Great Simba, what is this?
Stump Tooth It's your female! Run, Moja, run! The Devil-lion's after your blood.

They reach the cave

Moja (*seeing the cubs*) And what are these?
Stump Tooth They're your latest litter. Oh, Simba, (*falling to his knees*) I've been a bad lion, I've stolen the prey of my friends, spent too much time lying in the sun and generally wasted my days on earth. Spare us the wrath of the Devil-lion and I swear I'll become a reformed character.
Moja Be quiet! How can I think with you making all that noise? We don't know if it is the Devil-lion yet.
Stump Tooth It is, it is! Who else would kill your entire brood like that. Look at the shadows cast by his waving mane, and the flashes of light from his paws.
Moja Perhaps you're right. Mother of Simba and all the saint lions, what am I to do?
Stump Tooth (*praying*) Panthera leo, who art in heaven ...
Moja (*shouting*) I say, you up there, if you are the Devil-lion, listen to me!

The sound of the storm cuts out

Voice (*on amplifier*) What do you want?

Stump Tooth He spoke! Oh, Simba, though I walk through the valley of predatory-death, I shall fear no evil——

Moja I want to talk to you!

Voice What about?

Moja Are you really the Devil-lion or just some imposter?

An enormous roll of laughter which is echoed in rumbles of thunder

Voice My name is Thunder!

Moja That seems a funny name for a lion.

Voice My flying mane makes the whole world go dark. See, see how dark it is, and yet the sun has already scaled the sky for half a day. My giant paws flatten the ground and all the grazing fields for miles. As for my voice——

Moja Yes, yes, we know all about that. Let me see your face!

Voice —it deafens all who hear it.

Moja Well, there are some who say empty vessels make the most noise. Let me see your face and then I'll know whether to be afraid or not. (*Aside*) I'm only a small lion but he's not going to take my kingdom just by making a lot of noise. (*Calling*) Hey, you up there!

Voice How dare you!

Moja You know what the saying is. If a baby crawls under a bed and sits there, it'll grow up to be a dwarf. How do I know that's not what you are?

Voice What? Are you calling me a dwarf?

Stump Tooth (*all is lost*) Oh, Moja, what a fool you are ...

Moja Yes! Unless you let me see your face.

Thunder. The face of the Devil is seen—projection on to gauze or smoke

Voice There! look on my face and tremble.

Stump Tooth lets out a groan and buries his face. Even Moja is shaken

Moja Oh, Simba, show me what to do. Even I cannot hope to stand up to a demon like that.

1st Assistant And then he remembered something else.

Moja Stamp, Stump Tooth, stamp as if your life depended on it. (*He jumps to his feet and starts stamping loudly*)

Stump Tooth What is this, Moja? Have you gone *bata*?

1st Assistant Bats.

Moja Of course I haven't, I'm trying to shake the devil from the sky.

1st Assistant Moja had remembered something that the Ancients had said. Even the smallest movement can cause small winds that grow and grow and alter the whole behaviour of the sky. Of course it can take years and years.

Moja Stamp, Stump Tooth. Stamp everybody!

Stump Tooth begins to stamp. Soon everybody is stamping, spectators, even the Lioness and the cubs

Voice (*alarmed*) What is this? What are you up to down there?
Moja We're trying to shake you down like a rotten apple out of the sky. Come down here and face us, lion to lion!
All (*separately*) Yes, yes, come down here ... *etc.*

More stamping. Wind and thunder return to a crescendo, and then break off

Moja It's worked, it's worked.

A pause. The Devil-lion leaps into the clearing, wearing a demon mask and carrying an elaborate spear

Stump Tooth (*a shriek*) Oh, Simba, save us! (*He hides his face again*)
All (*separately*) Now's your chance, Moja. Kill him ... *etc.*
Moja (*aside*) Panthera leo, he's even worse than I thought. (*Aloud*) Jambo, Devil-king. Are you the one who wishes to take my kingdom from me?
Voice (*still on amplifier, but accompanied by mimed gestures by the masked demon*) Beware, Moja. You have defied my wrath and even shaken me like an apple from the sky. You cannot hope for mercy. Now I shall kill you.

The drums start. The stylized fight commences. Moja is unarmed, the Devil-lion uses his spear. The dancers cheer on Moja. Stump Tooth risks a glance or two and then with a cry goes back to his praying. After a great deal of leaping, shouting, spinning and grappling, Moja succeeds in grasping the spear and breaking it. Then he holds both points to the Devil's throat

Moja See what I've done. Now, Devil-lion, your days are numbered.
Voice Spare me, Moja. Let me go back to my sweet sky and I swear I'll never visit your country again.
Moja Very well, be gone. Remember it was I, Moja, Number One, King of the lions of Serengeti who has driven you from this place, and never show your mane or claws here again.

The Devil scurries off

Everybody cheers. Moja takes his bow very grandly. The sun comes out

Stump Tooth The sun, the sun! Oh, Moja, I promise I'll never, never doubt your courage again.

Moja (*grandly*) *Yes, I was rather good, wasn't I?* (*Aside*) Thank Simba he doesn't know I was like a jelly inside.

1st Assistant So Moja drove the demon Thunder from his land and ruled unchallenged for the rest of his days. Unfortunately this meant that the Serengeti hardly gets any rain these days and an awful lot of animals die of thirst, but can you have a lot of good without at least a pinch of evil?

Moja I am Moja. My roaring fills the plains and raises the dust where the crops used to grow. Know what it says when you hear the sound ...

Amplified sound effect of lions' roaring

Who is the King of the Jungle? I am ... I am ... I am!

Applause

THE MONSTER THAT ATE 3B
by Randall Lewton

As the title suggests, this is a lively comedy with opportunities for mime and improvisation. Class 3B are on holiday in Pericolo di Morte, Italy, where a sea-beast has been terrorizing the town.

Set: The town square in Pericolo di Morte, Italy. Period: modern.

Cast: 14 speaking parts. Extras.
Mayor of Pericolo di Morte. Giuseppe. Italian Boy. Italian Woman. Italian Man. Headmaster, with pupils from 3B. Carlo and Carla, the Goldonis, hotel owners. 1st Man. 2nd Man. Priest. 3rd Man. Mr Heywood, a teacher with 3B. Fletch, a pupil from 3B. Other pupils from 3B. Townspeople: old women, men at street café tables, old men playing dominoes, little children chasing about, ice-cream sellers, mothers hanging out washing, etc.

Playing time: 11 minutes.

Pericolo di Morte. The town square

Loud Italian music. Suddenly there are shouting Italians everywhere—priests, old women dressed in black, ice-cream sellers, men at street café tables, old men playing dominoes, little children chasing about, mothers hanging out washing across the auditorium, etc. etc.

A "mime", all in shouted gibberish Italian, of "typical" Italian street life:

Two men in a café are having a loud argument
A mother tells off a "cool"-looking teenager to the amusement of his friends
The old men and the teenagers exchange abuse
One boy kicks a football, dirtying the washing, which leads to a big chase
Carlo brings drinks out to the men at tables and sits down to join them
Carla emerges from the hotel and hands him the hotel sign to hang up
Carlo does so with a ladder and the shouted encouragement of the men

The Mayor enters pursued by a shouting crowd. He climbs on to a rostrum. He eventually quietens everybody down

Mayor Quiet! Quiet! Silenzio! My friends! We must be calm. We must think. This
   is a crisis for our town and we must use reason, argument, not hysteria.

They are all calm

   (*Hysterically*) What are we going to do?!

They all erupt again. Eventually one voice is heard over the others

Giuseppe It is the curse of Pericolo!
Mayor Quiet. Quiet.
Giuseppe It is the curse of Pericolo!
Mayor What's that you say, Giuseppe?
Giuseppe It is the curse of Pericolo di Morte!
Mayor Giuseppe, no-one believes that old story any more.

Adults shake their heads

Giuseppe (*cackling*) You would like to forget the curse but it is not so easy. You
   pretend that it is superstition. You pretend that we no longer believe.
Mayor Giuseppe, we don't have time to listen to your fairy-tales.
Giuseppe The curse is alive today.
Mayor Please, Giuseppe, we must decide——
Giuseppe Ask the children! They know of the curse. They know it is real! (*He grabs
   a boy*) Tell them. The curse of Pericolo. Tell them the old story that no-one believes.
Boy No, signore. Per favore.
Giuseppe Tell them!
Boy There is the legend of the curse of Pericolo and the sea-beast.

*All the townspeople scream involuntarily at the mention of the beast. They then try to
turn this into a scornful dismissive laugh. This they do each time the boy mentions
the beast*

Giuseppe Go on.
Boy They say that it was many hundreds of years ago. The people of Pericolo were
   very poor, close to starvation. One day a rich merchant was passing through the
   village ...

Music. The rest of the story is shown in mime:

*Two villagers meet the merchant who is displaying his wealth ostentatiously. They
become more and more annoyed and greedy at his behaviour. Eventually they attack
and murder the merchant. As they remove his jewellery other villagers arrive, are
horrified at first, then join in robbing the man. They cart off the body*

They threw the body into the sea, knowing that the tides here would carry it far out to sea. It was many months before the next victim stopped in the town ...

In mime the villagers surround and kill him

At first they had been driven by hunger, but soon they were moved only by greed. More and more frequent were their brutal crimes ...

Mime: A series of improvised quickfire comic murders by various means. When they uncover the last body and remove his cloak they shrink back in horror. They have killed a priest

They had killed a priest. On that day, it is said, the black curse fell on Pericolo. On that day came—the sea-beast.

Scream. Laugh

Each day it came to the town to claim new victims. Many were killed. The villagers feared to go near the shore. There could be no more fishing. The town was poorer than ever before. The people prayed for forgiveness. All that they had stolen they gave to the church. Some went on a pilgrimage to Rome. It is said that the curse was then broken. But some say that every hundredth year the sea-beast——

Scream. Laugh

—the sea-beast——

Scream. Laugh

—it returns so that the people of Pericolo shall never forget the crimes of their forefathers.
Giuseppe Do you still tell me that no-one believes in the sea-beast?

Scream. Laugh

Mayor Are you trying to ruin us all?

The crowd erupts

Silenzio! We must forget all about such superstitions. There is no curse of Pericolo di Morte.
Woman What about my little Salvatore? My angel!
Man We don't *know* how he died.
Woman It was the sea-beast——

Scream. Laugh

We all know it was the sea-beast. It has returned and it has taken my Salvatore and the others.

The crowd erupts

Mayor Quiet! All this talk of sea-beasts and curses. This wild talk must stop. It will spread. If it reaches the newspapers there will be no visitors this year. Who will bring his children here to be eaten by a sea-beast?

The Head enters with pupils

Head Excuse me. Per favore, where is the Hotel Calamari? We were expecting to be met at the station ... stazione.

Carla emerges from the crowd

Carla Benvenuto, signore. Carlo!

Carlo emerges

What is the time?
Carlo Five o'clock, cara mia.
Carla What time are you to meet the train?
Carlo (*guilty*) At four-thirty, cara mia.
Carla (*battering him*) Imbecile. Why did I marry such an imbecile? It is a wonder we have any business at all. If it were left to you, we would be bankrupt. Take the bags.

During the following, Carlo struggles under mountains of the pupils' luggage, taking it into the hotel

I am so sorry, signore. My husband, he is not right in the head. Welcome to Pericolo. (*She shrieks with delight as she looks at the pupils*) What beautiful children! (*She hugs and kisses each one*) Welcome to Italy. Bei ragazzi. Come in. Come in. You must be hungry. I have something very special for you. Come in. Come in.

They are shepherded inside

Woman This is wicked. They must not stay. They must not go near the sea. They will die like my Salvatore. Send them away.
1st Man Don't be a fool. If we send them away we will arouse suspicions.
2nd Man And if one of these English children is killed like the others?

Giuseppe His blood will be on our hands.

Mayor Nobody will be killed. All this talk of killing!

Priest If they stay we must not allow them near the beach. It is too dangerous. We must close the beach to all.

Mayor Father, here we have no ancient monuments, we have no mountains, no volcanoes, no beauty spots. Our visitors come only because we have the finest beach in the region. If we close the beach they will leave and no more will come.

2nd Man And will they come when one of these English children is killed?

3rd Man We must take this chance. Three are dead. Perhaps it is over for this time. Perhaps it has returned to the deep.

2nd Man You cannot take chances with the lives of children.

3rd Man And what of our lives, our children? How will we live if no visitors come? Last winter was hard—but what of next winter? Will the bank wait, eh, Roberto, or will you lose your café? When you cannot pay for your van, Stefano, how will you earn your living? We cannot exist without the summer tourists.

Mayor Federico is right. We have no choice.

The crowd shouts agreement

Priest Let us pray that we have made the right decision.

All Amen.

They disperse. A mime:

> *The Head and pupils emerge from the hotel and are seated at tables and fed huge quantities of spaghetti and ice-cream. Carla kisses and hugs them as she serves. Carlo does a slapstick routine with plates of food*

Heywood arrives

As he approaches the hotel, Giuseppe accosts him to warn him

Giuseppe (*grabbing Heywood*) You must go! Leave at once!

Heywood (*exhausted*) I've only just arrived!

Giuseppe Take the children away from here. The town is cursed.

Heywood What are you talking about? Take your hands off me. Why do the loonies always pick on me? What's Italian for "take a running jump"?

Giuseppe Listen to me, signore. You must go. If you stay here you will die. The children will die. The name of this town is death. Go. Do not wait. Visit Roma or Napoli. They are beautiful cities. Here is nothing for you—except the beach and in Pericolo di Morte the beach is too close to the cemetery. (*He cackles bitterly*) Go at once. There is a train in half an hour. Back to the station.

He starts to drag Heywood back to the station. Heywood resists. It turns into a comic tussle. Heywood ends up prone, being dragged towards the station by his feet, clawing with his hands. Giuseppe has continued talking

Venice is very nice at this time of year. And you will love Florence. Go. Wherever you go you must not stay here. We don't want you here. Stay and you die. You die, signore. You die. The sea-beast. The sea-beast.

The Head notices Heywood and comes across. The struggle continues

Head Heywood, what on earth are you doing?
Heywood I'm enjoying that warm Italian hospitality you were telling me about. Will you get this madman off me?
Head I say, old chap, signore, amico. Would you mind, my friend has had a very hard day ... Il mio amico ...
Heywood Don't reason with him! Hit him.
Head I don't know whether that would be a very good idea. He might be a godfather.
Heywood What has his family got to do with it? Get him off me!

The Head makes a very tentative effort

Carla arrives

Carla Ey, Giuseppe!

She batters him, screaming in gibberish Italian. He gets up and screams back. They continue for two minutes. The pupils all gather round as do the Italians. At the end Carla and Giuseppe part and everyone applauds enthusiastically. Now the muttered discussions the Italians have been having in pairs become louder and louder. They develop into full-scale rows which continue loudly during ...

Heywood That's all very quaint and interesting but we've all had a long day and it is time we were all in bed.
Fletch What are we doing tomorrow, sir?
Head The first thing I want to do is to get a nice sun-tan. So bright and early tomorrow we'll be off to the beach.

On the word "beach" the Italians all stop arguing simultaneously, turn towards the Head and let out a shriek. A dramatic chord. Black-out

OLIVER TWIST
adapted by Jeremy Brock
from the novel by Charles Dickens

This is a lively adaptation of Charles Dickens's novel, and the extract is set at a quiet bookstall in Clerkenwell. Oliver is being educated in the art of picking pockets by two of Fagin's professionals. The stage setting will need careful planning and inventiveness.

Set: A quiet street in Clerkenwell, London. Period: early Victorian.

Cast: 13 characters. Extras.
Oliver Twist, new to Fagin's den. The Artful Dodger, Fagin's senior boy. Charley, one of Fagin's urchins, a girl. Mr Brownlow, a gentleman at the bookstall. Passers-by. Mr Fang, the Magistrate. Two Clerks of Court. A Policeman. Fagin. Bill Sikes. Nancy, his girl-friend, here dressed like a prim little housewife. Witness, the bookstall keeper. Monks, Oliver's brother.

Playing time: 16 minutes.

Clerkenwell

A quiet street. A bookstall and a few Passers-by. A gentleman, Mr Brownlow, stands by one of the stalls, his face buried in a book

The Dodger, Charley and Oliver enter from the other side of the stage. Spotting Mr Brownlow, The Dodger pulls them up

Oliver What's the matter?
The Dodger Quiet. See that toffee-nose at the bookstall? He'll do.
Charley Ripe as a plum.

Music—a deep single note. Oliver is frozen to the spot. Everything turns to slow-motion as The Dodger and Charley creep up to Mr Brownlow's side. A simple switch and the gentleman's wallet is in The Dodger's hands. Still in slow-motion, Charley and The Dodger cross to the other side of the stage. They turn to find Oliver still frozen. As if in a silent movie, they cry out to him, but Oliver can hear nothing.

Slowly, slowly Mr Brownlow realizes his wallet is missing. He looks up to see Oliver staring like a terrified animal. Suddenly everything returns to real time

Mr Brownlow Stop! Thief!

Cartoonesque music. The chase. Oliver runs off then stops in a blind panic, turns and runs in the opposite direction as, one after another, the Passers-by rear out of the shadows and join the chase. They point exaggeratedly, like cartoon characters

Passer-by 1 Stop thief!
Passer-by 2 Stop thief!
Passer-by 3 Stop thief!
Passer-by 4 Stop thief!
Passer-by 5 Stop thief!
The Dodger Stop thief!
Charley Stop thief!

Oliver is chased all over the theatre: over the stalls, through the wings, down the aisles and finally back on to the stage while every free actor takes up the cry of "Stop thief!" Just as he thinks he has reached an empty stage and safety, he turns to find a crowd of silent, menacing Chasers, grinning and waiting. They knock him down

Passer-by 1 Stand aside!
Passer-by 2 Where's the gentleman?
Passer-by 3 Coming down the street, there.
Passer-by 4 Give him a little air!
Passer-by 1 Nonsense, he don't deserve it!
Passer-by 2 Make room for the gentleman!

Mr Brownlow puffs up and the crowd parts to let him in

Oliver lies pole-axed on the ground, his mouth bleeding and his eyes staring wildly

Passer-by 2 Is this the boy, sir?
Mr Brownlow Yes, I'm afraid it is.

The men in the crowd cheer loudly, fists raised in soccer-salutes. Oliver is yanked up

The Dodger and Charley exit unnoticed by the others

Passer-by 1 Stand on your legs, you devil!
Oliver It wasn't me, sir! It was two other boys! It wasn't me!
Passer-by 1 Shut your mouth!
Passer-by 2 I know him. He's a regular little thief.

Mr Brownlow Take him to the magistrate.

Everyone exits except Oliver and Mr Brownlow

The Lights change

Mr Fang, the Magistrate, enters. He is a giant on stilts, dressed in a huge robe of office and flanked by two Clerks of Court

A Policeman follows

Clerk of Court Silence in court! This court is now in session.
Officer (*to Oliver*) Stand up straight before the bench!

Mr Brownlow bows and offers his card to one of the Clerks of Court. He retreats with a gentlemanly nod of the head and waits to be questioned. Mr Fang glances at the card, then at Mr Brownlow

Mr Fang Who are you?!
Mr Brownlow (*pointing at his card*) My card, sir.
Mr Fang Officer, who is this fellow!?
Mr Brownlow My name, sir, is Brownlow.
Mr Fang What's he charged with?
Officer He's not charged at all, your worship. He appears against the boy, your worship.
Mr Fang Appears against the boy, does he?
Mr Brownlow Your worship ...
Mr Fang Hold your tongue, sir!
Mr Brownlow I beg your pardon?!
Mr Fang Hold your tongue this instant! How dare you bully a magistrate!
Mr Brownlow Well, I ...
Mr Fang One more word and I'll have you turned out of court. (*He turns on Oliver*) Who is this?
Officer This is the villain, your worship, who stole this gentleman's wallet.
Mr Fang (*leaning forward*) He did, did he?
Oliver Please, sir.
Mr Brownlow If I might be permitted ...
Clerk Silence in court!
Mr Brownlow Really I have never ...
Mr Fang I will not warn you again, sir. One more word and you pervert the course of justice! (*He turns to Oliver*) There is no punishment too severe for those who steal another man's property. You are charged with the theft of one watch, one snuff-box and one gold pen, for which crime I sentence you to ...

All in the courthouse freeze

> *The Dodger and Fagin enter. Fagin's hands are around The Dodger's neck. A terrified Charley follows—at a safe distance*

Fagin Where's Oliver?
The Dodger (*choking*) Let go of me will you!
Charley Mr Fagin, you're killing him!
Fagin Speak out, damn you, or I will kill you! (*He shakes him*) Will you not speak?
The Dodger The coppers have got him and that's all there is!

Fagin lunges at him, but The Dodger skips aside

> *Sikes enters and Fagin runs straight into him*

Sikes What's up with you?
Fagin The police have got Oliver!
Sikes When?
The Dodger Just now. We was attacked by a force of twenty officers or more!
Charley We were lucky to get away ourselves.
Fagin The boy could talk.
Sikes More than likely. They've got you now, Fagin.
Fagin And I'm afraid, if the game's up with us, it might be up with a good many more and it would be rather worse for you than it would for me.

Sikes grabs Fagin by the coat and practically lifts him off the ground. Fagin smiles blandly until Sikes, defeated, lets him down

Sikes Where's the boy now?
The Dodger The courthouse.
Sikes If he hasn't grassed yet there's no fear till he comes out again. When he does, he must be taken care of.
The Dodger How?
Sikes How would I know! (*To Fagin*) Think.
Fagin (*to The Dodger*) Think.
The Dodger (*to Charley*) Think.
Charley I'm thinking.

> *Sikes, Fagin, The Dodger and Charley exit*

The courthouse comes alive

Mr Fang ... two years' hard labour in the colony of Australia!

Oliver falls to the floor in a dead faint. Mr Brownlow rushes forward to help

Mr Fang He's shamming! Let him lie there. He'll soon come round.
Mr Brownlow This is outrageous!
Mr Fang Clear the court!

A witness enters, breathless with running

Witness Don't take him away!
Mr Fang Who is this? Turn this person out!
Witness Your worship, I saw the theft! I keep the bookstall where this gentleman was reading. I saw three boys, two other boys and the prisoner here, loitering in the street. This boy was frozen to the spot. The robbery was committed by another boy, I swear to you. I saw it done!
Mr Fang The prosecutor was reading, was he?
Witness Yes sir, the book he has in his hand.
Mr Fang Is it paid for?
Witness No sir.
Mr Brownlow Dear me, I quite forgot.
Mr Fang A nice person to bring a charge against a poor defenceless child. I consider, sir, that you obtained possession of that book under very suspicious and disreputable circumstances and you may think yourself very fortunate that the owner of the property declines to prosecute. The boy is discharged. Clear the court!
Mr Brownlow Damn me!
Mr Fang Clear the court!

Mr Fang and the two Clerks of Court exit

The Lights change

Mr Brownlow picks Oliver up and dusts him down with a sad shake of the head

They exit

Nancy enters, dressed like a prim little housewife with a straw bonnet and a little basket

Sikes, Charley, The Dodger and Fagin follow. She gives them a twirl

The Dodger A proper little lady!
Nancy I got it from one of my gentlemen.
Fagin Are you certain they'll fall for it?
Nancy Have I ever let you down?

Sikes She's a honour to her sex and I intend to drink her health!
Charley (*aside*) He'd drink the health of a copper if it meant free grog.
Fagin Wait. Take this door-key. It makes you look respectable. There.

Nancy takes the door key and hangs it on her right hand forefinger. She strikes a pose

Fagin Very good. Very good indeed. You know what to do?
Nancy Only the same as what I do all night. Pretend.

She smiles, flicks her skirts and they all exit

Mr Brownlow and Oliver enter. Oliver's head is bandaged and he walks with a slight limp. As Mr Brownlow talks, the Gang begin closing in behind them, always just out of vision. When Oliver senses something and turns, they melt into the background or freeze into poses of city-indifference. It is like a truly threatening game of Grandma's Footsteps of which Mr Brownlow is blissfully ignorant

Mr Brownlow Never in my life have I witnessed such rudeness! Tomorrow I shall write to Lord Salisbury and voice my anger in language of the sternest kind. But I am forgetting myself. We must look to your needs first. Now then, are you hungry?
Oliver Yes, sir.
Mr Brownlow Mrs Bedwin, my housekeeper, will give you some good strong broth. I take it that's what you eat?
Oliver Yes, sir.
Mr Brownlow Good, good. Nothing too rich, if your stomach is not familiar. I have a small room that I keep for guests which I would be delighted to offer to you. What do you say to that, eh?

Nancy rushes on stage before Oliver can speak and throws her arms around his neck

The Gang keep watch, from a safe distance

Nancy Oh, my dear brother!
Oliver Let go of me!
Nancy Oh my gracious, I've found him! Thank you, sir, thank you. Oh, you naughty boy!
Oliver Let go of me!
Mr Brownlow Is this child your brother?
Nancy My very own, sir!
Oliver I don't know her!
Nancy Why Oliver, it's your own Nancy!
Oliver Nancy?

Nancy You see! He knows me. He can't blame himself. Make him come home sir. He'll kill his poor mother and father!

Oliver She's not my sister!

Nancy Only hear him!

Oliver I don't know her!

Nancy Come, Oliver. Come home to your poor mother, you young scoundrel!

Oliver I have no mother!

Nancy Oh, you little wretch! Have a heart, sir I beg you.

Mr Brownlow Oliver. You must return to your family at once.

Nancy My poor brother! Sir, how can I thank you enough?

Mr Brownlow Please. Be a good child, Oliver.

Oliver She's not——

Nancy (*covering Oliver's mouth*) Thank you, sir, thank you.

A bemused Mr Brownlow exits

Nancy holds on to Oliver just long enough, then lets go. She is clearly not happy with what she has done

Oliver tears US *straight into the arms of Fagin*

Fagin (*holding a club*) Delighted to see you again, Oliver. I'm so sorry we were parted.

Oliver breaks and runs DS *straight into the arms of Sikes who hurls him back towards the Gang*

Nancy No, Bill!

Nancy is held back as the Gang close in, forming a tight semi-circle, all eyes on Fagin

Fagin So. You wanted to get away, did you? Wanted to get assistance, call for the police? We'll cure you of that my young master.

Fagin raises the club but Nancy takes it from him and hurls it off stage

Nancy I won't stand by and see it done, Fagin! You've got the boy. What more would you have? Let him be or, I swear to God, I'll mark you myself!

Sikes What the devil do you mean, interfering in a man's business?

Nancy Leave him be! Can't you see he's sick? (*To the Gang*) Are you such cowards you'll stand by and watch this cruelty?

Fagin (*snapping*) Bill!

Sikes (*grabbing Nancy*) Come here!

Nancy I will not stand by and see it done!

Sikes (*slapping her across the face*) What are you? (*Up close*) Do you know what you are?

Nancy Ay, I know what I am! And I wish I'd been struck dead in the street before I played your sneak. (*She points at Oliver*) That boy is a thief, a liar, a devil and all that's bad from this night forth. Isn't that enough without blows?

Fagin (*aside*) Civil words, Bill, civil words.

Silence

Sikes (*aside to Nancy*) I'll deal with you later.

Nancy exits

Fagin motions to the Gang and they exit

Fagin (*with a sigh*) One happy family again.

Gradually the Lights change to a spotlight on Oliver. Fagin kneels down—the kindly father

Why do you do this to me? Did I not take you in, feed you, give you new friends to play with? I loved you like my own. Is this how you thank me? Deny all knowledge of me? Try to run away? I had a young girl once who ran to the police. Silly child. What choice did I have, after such treacherous behaviour, but to reveal her to the Crown as a thief? They hanged her, Oliver. She was eleven. We're your family now. We care about you. Shall we be friends? Eh? Just you and me, eh?

Oliver freezes

Monks enters

Monks Well sir? Does the boy turn?

Fagin Ah. He's not quite so easy as I thought.

Monks (*threatening*) Remember your promise, sir.

Fagin Be patient, my friend. Corruption finds his own time. I've had my eye on him, close ... very close. Once let him feel that he is one of us. Once fill his mind with the idea that he has been a thief, and he is ours! Ours for life!

Monks Yours, sir. Not mine.

Fagin Mine, then. Yes, indeed. Mine. (*He chuckles*) But are not my interests also yours, my friend? Or you would not have come to me.

Silence

Monks Ruin him.

Music

Black-out

OUR DAY OUT
by Willy Russell

A group of underprivileged schoolchildren board the coach for a school outing from Liverpool into Wales. There is conflict between two members of the staff: the forward-thinking, sympathetic Mrs Kay and the dictatorial Mr Briggs who gradually relaxes as the day progresses.

Set: The school gates, on the coach, on the beach, on a cliff.

Cast: M3 F2, 7 boys 3 girls. Extras.
The Driver. Teachers: Mrs Kay, early 40s; Susan, early 20s; Colin, early 20s; Briggs, early 30s. Kids: Carol, 13; Reilly, 15; Digga, 15; Linda, 15; Karen, 15; Andrews, 13; Ronson, 13; Kevin, 12; Jimmy, 12; Maurice, 12; and others.

Playing time: 18 minutes.

Driver (*heaving off a kid who managed to get on to the bus*) Get off of my bus.

Mrs Kay Is there something the matter, Driver?

Driver Are these children in your charge, madam?

Mrs Kay Yes.

Driver Well, you haven't checked them have y'?

Mrs Kay Checked them? Checked them for what?

Driver Chocolate and lemonade! We don't allow it. I've seen it on other coaches madam; fifty-two vomitin' kids, it's no joke. I'm sorry, but we don't allow that.

Mrs Kay (*to Susan*) Here comes Mr Happiness. All right Driver, I'll check them for you. Now listen, everyone: if anyone has brought chocolate or lemonade with them I want them to put up their hands.

A sea of innocent faces and unraised hands

There you are Driver, all right?

Driver No, it's not right. Y' can't just take their word for it. They have to be searched. You can't just believe kids.

Pause. Mrs Kay could blow up but she doesn't

Mrs Kay Can I have a word with you, Driver, in private?

The Driver comes off the coach. She manoeuvres it so that the Driver has his back to the kids and other teachers

What's your name, Driver?
Driver Me name? I don't usually have to give me name.
Mrs Kay Oh, come on. What's your name?
Driver Schofield, Ronnie Schofield.
Mrs Kay Well, Ronnie (*pointing*), just take a look at those streets.

As the Driver looks Mrs Kay motions, behind his back, indicating that the other teachers should get the kids on to the coach

Ronnie, would you say they were the sort of streets that housed prosperous parents?
Driver We usually do the better schools.
Mrs Kay All right, you don't like these kids, I can see that. But do you really have to cause them so much pain?
Driver What have I said? I only told them to wait.
Mrs Kay Ronnie, the kids with me today don't know what it is to *look* at a bar of chocolate. Lemonade, Ronnie? Lemonade never touches their lips. (*We should almost hear the violins*) These are the children, Ronnie, that stand outside shop windows in the pouring rain, looking and longing, but never getting. Even at Christmas time, when your kids from the better schools are singing carols, opening presents, these kids are left outside, left to wander the cold cruel streets.

The Driver is grief-stricken. Behind him, in the coach the kids are stuffing themselves stupid with sweets, chocolate and lemonade. Mrs Kay leaves the Driver to it and climbs on board. As the Driver turns to board the coach all evidence of sweets and lemonade immediately disappears. The Driver puts his hand in his pocket and produces a few quid

Driver (*to a kid on the front seat*) Here y'are son, run to the shops an see what sweets y' can get with that.
Susan (*leaning across*) What did you say?
Mrs Kay Lied like hell, of course. (*She gets up and faces the kids*) Now, listen everyone. Listen. We'll be setting off for the Conway in a couple of minutes.

Cheers from everyone

Listen. Now, we want everybody to enjoy themselves today and so I don't want any silly squabbling and I don't want anybody doing anything dangerous either to yourselves or to others. That's the only rule we're going to have today, think of yourselves, but think of others as well.

Reilly and Digga come rushing on to the coach

Reilly Miss, we're comin', Miss, we're comin' with y' ...
Mrs Kay Where's the note, Brian?
Reilly He didn't give us one, Miss. He's comin' himself. He said to wait.

Reilly and Digga go down the aisle to the back of the coach

Colin He's coming to keep an eye on us.
Susan To make sure we don't enjoy ourselves.
Mrs Kay Well, I suppose we'll just have to deal with him the best way we can.

Mrs Kay sits down, next to Carol. Reilly and Digga go to the back seat

Reilly (*to a little kid on the back seat*) Right. You. Move.
Little Kid Why?
Reilly 'Cos we claimed the back seat, that's why.
Little Kid You're not even in the Progress, though.

Briggs gets on to the coach, unseen by Reilly and Digga

Digga 'Ey, hardfaced, we used to be, so shift!
Reilly Now move before I mince y'.

Briggs glares at the Kids. All the Kids spot a cloud on the blue horizon

Briggs (*barking, suddenly*) Reilly, Dickson sit down!
Reilly Sir, we was only ——
Briggs (*staccato*) I said sit, lad, now move.

Reilly and Digga sit on the little kid who is forced out. He stands, exposed in the aisle, terrified of Briggs

   Sit down. What you doing, lad, what you doing?
Little Kid Sir, Sir, Sir. ... Sir, I haven't got a seat. (*He is almost in tears*)
Briggs Well, find one, boy, find one!

Colin gets out of his seat and indicates to the kid to sit there

Briggs (*to Mrs Kay*) You've got some real bright sparks here, Mrs Kay. A right
   bunch.
Mrs Kay Well, I think we might just manage to survive now that you've come to
   look after us.

Briggs The boss thought it might be a good idea if you had an extra member of staff. Looking at this lot I'd say he was right. There's a few of them I could sling off right now. (*Barking*) Linda Croxley, what are you doin'? Sit down, girl. (*He addresses all the kids*) Right! Now listen: we wouldn't like you to think that we don't want you to enjoy yourselves today, because we do. But a lot of you won't have been on a school outing before and therefore won't know *how* to enjoy yourselves. There'll be no shouting on this outing, will there? (*Screaming*) Will there?
Kids No, Sir.
Briggs No Sir, no Sir. Just stay in your seat. Be quiet, be good and behave!

The kid who went to get the sweets rushes on board loaded with bags

Kid I've got them. I've got loads.
Briggs Where've you been?
Kid Sir, gettin' sweets.
Briggs Sweets? SWEETS!
Mrs Kay (*reaching for the sweets*) Thank you, Maurice.

The Driver taps Briggs on the shoulder

Driver Can I have a word with you?
Briggs Pardon.
Driver In private.

The Driver leads the way off the coach. Briggs follows. Mrs Kay gives the sweets to Colin and Susan who start to dish them out

Kids (*variously*) Ooh, great. Give us one, Miss. What about me, Sir?
Driver (*outside the coach, to Briggs*) The thing is, about these kids, they're like little souls, lost an' wanderin' the cruel heartless streets ...

The Driver continues his lecture to Briggs outside the coach as the action switches back inside. Colin is at the back seat giving out sweets to Reilly and Co

Reilly How are y' gettin on with Miss, Sir?
Digga We saw y' Sir, goin' into that pub with her.

Further down the aisle Susan is watching and listening as she gives out sweets

Colin (*covering his embarrassment*) Did you?
Reilly Are you in love with her, Sir?
Colin (*making his escape*) All right, you've all got sweets have you?
Reilly (*jeering*) Sir's in love, Sir's in love. ...

Reilly laughs as Colin makes his way back along the aisle

Susan Watch it, Brian!
Reilly (*with feigned innocence*) What, Miss?
Susan You know what.
Reilly Agh hey, he is in love with y' though, isn't he, Miss?
Digga I'll bet he wants to marry y', Miss.
Reilly You'd be better off with me, Miss. I'm better lookin', an' I'm sexier.

Susan gives up playing it straight. She goes up to Reilly and whispers to him

Susan (*whispering*) Brian, little boys shouldn't try and act like men. The days might
  come when their words are put to the test! (*She walks away*)
Reilly Any day, Miss, any day.
Digga What did she say, what did she say?
Reilly She said she fancied me!

Briggs and the Driver come on board. Briggs goes to sit opposite Mrs Kay

Briggs Well ... We've got a right head-case of a driver.

*The engine comes to life. The Kids cheer. Briggs gives a warning look, then turns
away. As he does so we see a mass of hands raised in two-fingered gestures to anyone
who might be passing*

On the back seat the Little Kid overhears a conversation between Digga and Reilly

Digga Reilly, light up.
Reilly Where's Briggsy?
Digga Up the front. Y' all right, I'll keep the eye out for y'.
Little Kid Agh 'ey, you've got ciggies. I'm gonna tell Miss.
Digga Tell her. She won't do nothin' anyway.
Little Kid I'll tell Sir.
Reilly You do an' I'll gob y'.
Digga Come on, open that window you.
Little Kid Why?
Reilly Why d' y' think? So we can get a bit of fresh air.
Little Kid Well, there is no fresh air round here. You just want to smoke. An' smokin'
  stunts your growth.
Reilly I'll stunt your growth if y' don't get it open.

Andrews gets up and reaches obligingly for the window

Andrews I'll open it for y', Reilly.

Reilly ducks behind a seat and lights up

Andrews Gis a ciggie.
Reilly Sod off. Get y' own ciggies.
Andrews Ah, go on, I opened the window for y'.
Digga Be told you, y' not gettin' no ciggie.

Briggs leaves his seat at the front and heads towards the back of the coach

(*Whispering to Reilly*) Briggs!

Reilly quickly hands the cigarette to Andrews who, unaware of the approaching Briggs seizes it with enthusiasm

Andrews Ooh, thanks Reilly.

Andrews ducks behind the seat and takes a massive drag. He comes up to find Briggs gazing down at him and the ciggie

Briggs Put it out.
Andrews Sir, I wasn't ...
Briggs Put it out lad. Now get to the front of the coach.

Andrews gets up and makes his way to Briggs's seat as Briggs remains at the back

Briggs Was it your ciggie, Reilly?
Reilly Sir, swear on me mother I didn't ...
Digga Take no notice of him, Sir. How can he swear on his mother, she's been dead ten years.

Reilly is about to stick one on Digga

Briggs All right. All right! We don't want any argument. There'll be no smokin' if I stay up here will there?

Briggs takes Andrews's seat. Mrs Kay and Carol are sitting next to each other, Carol next to the window staring out of it

Carol Isn't it horrible, eh, Miss?
Mrs Kay Mm?
Carol Y' know, all the thingy like; the dirt an' that. (*Pause*) I like them nice places.
Mrs Kay Which places?
Carol Know them places on the telly with gardens, an' trees outside an' that.
Mrs Kay You've got trees in Pilot Street haven't you?

Carol They planted some after the riots. But the kids chopped them down an' burnt them on Bonfire Night. (*Pause*) Miss ... Miss, y' know when I grow up, Miss, y'know if I work hard an' learn to read an' write, would you think I'd be able to live in one of them nice places?

Mrs Kay (*putting her arm around her*) Well, you could try love, couldn't you eh?

Carol Yeh!

On the back seat Reilly and Digga are stifled by Briggs's presence

Briggs (*suddenly pointing out of the window*) Now, just look at that.

Digga and Reilly glance but see nothing to look at

Digga What?

Briggs (*disgustedly*) What? Can't you see? Look, those buildings, don't you ever observe what's around you?

Reilly It's only the docks, Sir.

Briggs You don't get buildings like that anymore. Just look at the work that must have gone into that.

Reilly Do you like it down here then, Sir?

Briggs I'm often down here at weekends, taking photographs. Are you listening, Reilly? There's a wealth of history that won't be here much longer.

Reilly My old feller used to work down here.

Briggs What did he think of it?

Reilly He hated it.

Briggs Well, you tell him to take another look and he might appreciate it.

Reilly I'll have a job—I haven't seen him for two years. (*He turns away and looks out of the window*)

A few seats further down Linda suddenly kneels up on her seat

Linda (*to Jackie*) Ooh, look, there's Sharron. (*She shouts and waves*) Sharron ... Sha ...

Briggs Linda Croxley!

Briggs gets up and moves towards Linda. Only at the last moment does she turn and sit "properly"

And what sort of an outfit is that supposed to be for a school visit?

Linda (*chewing; contemptuously; staring out of the window*) What?

Briggs Don't you "what" me, young lady.

Linda merely shrugs

You know very well that on school trips you wear school uniform.

Linda Well, Mrs Kay never say nott'n about it.
Briggs You're not talking to Mrs Kay now.
Linda Yeh, I know.
Briggs (*quietly but threateningly*) Now listen here, young lady, I don't like your attitude. I don't like it one bit.
Linda What have I said? I haven't said nott'n, have I?
Briggs I'm talking about your attitude.

She dismisses him with a glance and turns away

I'm telling you now, Miss. Carry on like this and when we get to Conway you'll be spending your time in the coach.
Linda I don't care, I don't wanna see no crappy castle anyway.
Briggs Just count yourself lucky you're not a lad. Now I'm warning. 'Cause any more unpleasantness on this trip and I shall see to it that it's the last you ever go on. Is that understood? Is it?
Linda (*sighing*) Yeh.
Briggs It better had be.

Briggs makes his way to the front of the coach and addresses the kid next to Andrews

Right, you, what's your name? Wake up.
Maurice Sir, me?
Briggs What's your name?
Maurice McNally, Sir.
Briggs Right, McNally, go and sit at the back.
Maurice Sir, I don't like the back.
Briggs Never mind what you like, go and sit at the back.

Maurice does so

Right, Andrews, shove up. How long have you been smoking, Andrews?
Andrews Sir, I don't ... Sir, since I was eight.
Briggs And how old are you now?
Andrews Sir, thirteen, Sir.
Briggs What do your parents say?
Andrews Sir, me mam says nothin' about it but when me dad comes home, Sir, Sir, he belts me.
Briggs Because you smoke?
Andrews No Sir, because I won't give him one.

Pause

Briggs Your father works away from home does he?

Andrews What? No, Sir.

Briggs You said, "when he comes home". I thought you meant he was away a lot.

Andrews He is. But he doesn't go to work.

Briggs Well, what does he do then?

Andrews I don't know, Sir, he just comes round every now an' then an' has a barney with me mam. Then he goes off again. I think he tries to get money off her but she won't give him it though. She hates him. We all hate him.

Briggs Listen, why don't you promise yourself you'll give up smoking? You must realize it's bad for your health.

Andrews Sir, I do, Sir. I've got a terrible cough.

Briggs Then why don't you pack it in?

Andrews Sir, I can't.

Briggs Thirteen and you can't stop smoking?

Andrews No, Sir.

Briggs (*sighing and shaking his head*) Well, you'd better not let me catch you again.

Andrews No, Sir. I won't.

Kids (*variously*) There's the tunnel, the Mersey tunnel, we're goin' through the tunnel. (*They cheer as the bus goes into the tunnel*)

Black-out to denote the passing of time. Then the Lights come up on the beach

During the Black-out, the Driver, Mrs Kay and some of the Kids exit. When the Lights come up they rush on playing football

Reilly and the others join the game. As Reilly scores Mrs Kay gives up being goalie

Mrs Kay Whooh. I've had enough, I'm all in.

Maurice Ah Miss, we've got no goalie now.

Susan and Colin approach the group

Mrs Kay Carol can go in goal. (*To Susan and Colin*) Where is she?

Susan Who?

The Kids all exit

Mrs Kay Carol. I thought she was with you.

Colin We haven't seen her for hours.

Mrs Kay I thought ... You haven't seen her at all?

Susan We thought she was here.

Mrs Kay (*looking around*) Oh, she couldn't, could she?

Susan Lost?

Mrs Kay Don't say it. Perhaps he's seen her. (*Shouting off to Briggs*) Mr Briggs ... Mr Briggs ...

Briggs enters

Briggs Is that it then? Are we going home?

Mrs Kay Have you seen Carol Chandler in the last hour?

Briggs I thought I'd make it quite plain that I was having nothing more to do with your outing.

Mrs Kay Have you seen Carol Chandler?

Briggs No, I haven't.

Mrs Kay I think she may have wandered off somewhere.

Briggs You mean you've lost her?

Mrs Kay No. I mean she might have wandered off somewhere!

Briggs Well what's that if it's not losing her? All I can say is it's a wonder you haven't lost half a dozen of them. (*He turns to go*)

Colin Listen, Briggs, it's about time someone told you what a berk you ——

Briggs (*wheeling on him*) And you listen! Sonny! Don't you try to tell me a thing, because you haven't even earned the right. Don't you worry, when we get back to school your number's up, as well as hers (*indicating Mrs Kay*). And you (*indicating Susan*). Yes. I saw what was going on between you and Reilly. When we get back I'll have the lot of you.

Mrs Kay Would you mind postponing your threats until we find Carol Chandler. At the moment I'd say the most important thing is to find the girl.

Briggs Don't you mean *try* to find her.

Mrs Kay Susan, you keep the rest of them playing football. We'll split up and look for her.

They go off in separate directions

We see Carol. She is standing on a cliff, looking out, waving at seagulls

Briggs appears on the cliffs and sees Carol

Briggs Carol Chandler, just come here. Who gave you permission to come on these cliffs?

Carol (*moving to the edge*) No-one. (*She turns, dismissing him*)

Briggs I'm talking to you, Miss Chandler.

Carol continues to ignore his presence

Now just listen here, young lady ——

Carol (*suddenly turning*) Don't you come near me!

Briggs (*taken aback by her vehemence he stops*) Pardon.

Carol I don't want you to come near me.

Briggs Well in that case just get yourself moving and let's get down to the beach.

Carol You go. *I'm* not comin'.

Briggs You what?

Carol Tell Mrs Kay she can go home without me. I'm stoppin' here, by the sea.

Pause

Briggs Now you just listen to me. I've had just about enough today, just about enough and I'm not putting up with a pile of silliness from the likes of you. Now come on!

He starts towards her but she moves to the very edge of the cliff

Carol Try an' get me an' I'll jump over.

Briggs is stopped in his tracks, astounded and angered

Briggs (*shouting*) Listen, you stupid girl, get yourself over here, this minute.

Carol ignores him

  I'll not tell you again!

They stare at each other. It's obvious that she will not do as he bids

Briggs I'll give you five seconds! Just five seconds, one, two, three, four—I'm warning you!—five.

Carol I've told y', I'm not comin' with y'. I *will* jump y' know. I will.

Briggs Just what are you tryin' to do to me?

Carol I've told y', just leave me alone an' I won't jump. (*Pause*) I wanna stay here where it's nice.

Briggs Stay here? How could you stay here? What would you do, eh? Where would you live?

Carol I'd be all right.

Briggs I've told you, stop being silly.

Carol (*turning on him*) What are you worried for eh? You don't care do y'? Do y'?

Briggs What? About you? Listen, if I didn't care, why would I be up here now, trying to stop you doing something stupid?

Carol Because if I jumped over, you'd get into trouble when you get back to school. That's why, Briggsy, so stop goin' on. You hate me.

Briggs Don't be ridiculous. Just because I'm a schoolteacher it doesn't mean to say that——

Carol Don't lie you! I know you hate me. I've seen you goin' home in your car, passin' us on the street. An' the way you look at us. You hate all the kids.

Briggs What ... Why do you say that?

Carol Why can't I just stay out here an' live in one of them nice white houses, an' do the garden an' that?

Briggs Look—Carol. You're talking as though you've given up on life. It sounds as though life for you is ending, instead of just beginning. Now why can't ... I mean, if that's what you want ... why can't ... what's to stop you working hard at school from now on, getting a good job and then moving out here when you're old enough? Eh?

Carol (*turning and looking at him with pure contempt*) Don't be so bloody stupid. (*She turns and looks out to the sea*) It's been a great day today. I loved it. I don't wanna leave here an' go home. (*Pause*) If I stayed it wouldn't be any good though, would it? You'd send the coppers to get me, wouldn't y'?

Briggs We'd have to. How would you survive out here?

Carol I know. (*Pause*) I'm not goin' back though. (*She kneels at the cliff edge and looks over*)

Briggs Carol, please.

Carol Sir, you know if you'd been my old feller—I would've been all right wouldn't I?

Briggs slowly and cautiously creeps forward, holding out his hand

Briggs Carol, please come away from there.

Carol looks down over the cliff

Please.

Carol Sir, Sir you don't half look funny y' know.

Briggs (*smiling*) Why?

Carol Sir, you should smile more often. You look great when y' smile.

Briggs (*holding out his hand*) Come on, Carol.

Carol Sir—what'll happen to me for doin' this?

Briggs Nothing. I promise.

Carol Sir, you're promisin' now, but what about back at school?

Briggs It won't even be mentioned, I promise.

His hand is outstretched. She decides to believe him and reaches out for his hand. As she does she slips but he manages to lunge forward and clasp her to safety. He stands with his arms wrapped around her

The other Kids are playing football. Reilly with the ball is trying to get past a huge row of defenders

Linda (*from the side of the game*) Go on, Brian, go on, go on. ...

Reilly scores

Yes!

Reilly preens himself for Linda

Mrs Kay enters with Susan, shaking her head

Mrs Kay I think we'd better let the police know.
Susan Shall I keep them playing?

Briggs and Carol join the group

Oh, he's found her.
Colin I'll bet he makes a bloody meal out of this.
Susan It doesn't matter. She's safe, that's the main thing.
Colin We'd better round them up. It'll be straight home now.

Colin begins to get the Kids together

Mrs Kay (*approaching Briggs and Carol*) Carol where were you?
Carol On the cliff, Miss.
Mrs Kay On the ...
Briggs It's all right, Mrs Kay, we've been through all that. Now. If you'll just let me deal with this.

Mrs Kay puts her arm around Carol

Mrs Kay Carol! The worry you've caused. Oh, love.
Briggs Come on. Everyone on the coach.
Driver Back to the school then?
Briggs School? Back to school? It's still early isn't it? Anyway—you can't come all the way to the seaside and not pay a visit to the fair.
Carol (*rushing to the other Kids*) We're goin' the fair, Sir's takin' us to the fair.

Briggs turns to Mrs Kay who still can't believe her ears

Briggs You never know Mrs Kay—play your cards right an' I might take you for a ride on the waltzer!

Black-out to denote the passing of time

Everybody forms into a group for Mrs Kay's camera, holding the note on the word "cheese". A cowboy hat is produced for Briggs to wear. In this pause the two bored girls are apart from the rest of the group

Bored 1 What d' y' think?
Bored 2 The fair?
Bored 1 Yeh.
Bored 2 (*considering*) Borin'!
Briggs Last one on the coach pays the fare.

The coach is now re-formed and nearly everyone is on board. Ronson runs up to the coach and Briggs who is standing waiting for him

Ronson Sir, that was great that, it was great.
Briggs Come on.
Ronson Sir, can we come again tomorrow?
Briggs Oh, get on the bus, Ronson.

The Kids on the coach are now mostly asleep or dozing. Briggs, wearing the cowboy hat, makes his way along the aisle. When he reaches Mrs Kay she turns the camera on him and takes a snapshot. It is as if in that moment the flashlight signals the beginning of a return to reality for Mr Briggs. He becomes conscious of the hat he is wearing and, smiling at Mrs Kay, removes it and places it on the head of the sleeping Carol, who is clutching a fairground goldfish. Mrs Kay puts the completed film into a canister. Briggs walks down the aisle

(*To Mrs Kay*) Well ... nearly home.
Mrs Kay (*indicating the film*) I've got some gems of you in here. We'll have one of these put up in the staff room when they're developed.
Briggs Eh? One of me? What for?
Mrs Kay Don't worry, I'm not going to let you forget the day you enjoyed yourself.
Briggs (*watching her put the canister into an envelope*) Look. Erm ... why don't you let me develop those? I could do them in the lab.
Mrs Kay I don't know—using school facilities for personal gain. (*She hands over the film*) Thank you.
Briggs Have them done as soon as I can. (*He sits down*)
Linda (*to Reilly*) Are y' glad y' came?
Reilly Yeh.
Linda It was great, wasn't it, eh?
Reilly It'll be the last trip I go on.
Linda Why?
Reilly Well I'm leavin' in the summer, aren't I?
Linda What y'gonna do?
Reilly Nothin' I suppose ... (*He looks out of the window*) It's bleedin' horrible when y' look at it isn't it?
Linda What?
Reilly (*nodding, indicating the city*) That. Liverpool.
Linda Yeh.

Underscoring ends as the coach stops

Briggs Right. Come on, everybody off.

Everybody is now off the coach. The Driver and various Kids have moved off. Reilly and Linda, arms around each other, pass Mr Briggs

Reilly Night, Sir. Enjoyed yourself today didn't y', Sir.
Briggs Pardon.
Reilly I didn't know you was like that, Sir. All right for a laugh an' that. See y' tomorrow, Sir.

Briggs nods goodbye to them and then suddenly calls after them

Briggs Oh—Linda.

She stops and turns

We, erm ... we'll let the uniform go this time. But don't let me catch you dressing like that again on a school outing.

Reilly and Linda exit

Bored 1 Wasn't that a great day?
Bored 2 It was cracker. Come on.

The two bored girls run off

Mrs Kay Well that seems to be it. (*She sees Carol hovering nearby*) Are you going home Carol?

From off we hear a whistle and the Driver enters

Driver Erm, excuse me madam, have you lost a small python?
Mrs Kay (*just for a second thinking, as do we, that it might be true*) What!

From behind his back the Driver produces the goldfish in the plastic bag

Driver (*as he hands it to Carol*) They always forget somethin'.
Mrs Kay Thanks, Ronny.
Driver Thanks, Helen. Good-night. (*To others as he exits*) Bye now. See y'.

The Driver exits

Colin ⎫
Susan ⎬ (*together*) Good-night.
Briggs ⎭

Mrs Kay Well, that's that. I don't know about anyone else but I'm for a drink.

Susan Oh, I'll second that.

Colin They'll just be open.

Mrs Kay (*to Briggs*) You going to join us?

Briggs Oh, well actually I've ...

Susan Oh come on.

Briggs No, I'd er ... I'd better not. Thanks anyway. I've got lots of marking to do at home. Thanks all the same.

Mrs Kay Well if we can't twist your arm—thanks for today.

Mrs Kay turns and leads the others off, failing to see Carol hovering in the shadows

Car's over here.

Mrs Kay, Colin and Susan exit

Briggs reaches into his pocket for his car keys. Along with the keys he brings out the package containing the film. He stands, looking at the package unaware of:

The Kids, Reilly, Andrews, Jackie, Carol, Digga, Maurice, Ronson, Milton, Linda, Little Kid, Boring Girls and every other one of them, appear individually from behind him and watch him

Carol walks forward out of the shadows as Briggs suddenly makes his decision and exposes the role of film. He turns and sees Carol watching him along with all the other kids. Carol moves off as if to go home

Parent (*off*) Carol! Where've you been? Just get in this bloody house.

THE PLAY OF THE ROYAL ASTROLOGERS
by Willis Hall

The Emperor has had four chests of gold stolen, and he has decided that an astrologer will be able to find the thieves. In this scene, the indolent Father Mole-Cricket, who happened to mention that astrology might help him make money, and his lazy son, have four days in which to find the Emperor's stolen gold.

Set: The Mole-Cricket back garden, with a small veranda.

Cast: 9 characters.
Father Mole-Cricket, a lazy character who dabbles in astrology. Mother Mole-Cricket, his exasperated wife. Master Mole-Cricket, equally lazy like his father. The Emperor, a short and fussy monarch. His Chancellor, a tall harassed man, with a long beard. The First Thief, the leader. The Second Thief. The Third Thief. The Fourth Thief.

Playing time: 18 minutes.

The Mole-Cricket back garden. We discover Father Mole-Cricket sitting dejectedly in the garden and Master Mole-Cricket leaning against the veranda. Mother Mole-Cricket is sweeping the veranda with a broom. She pauses in her task to lean over the veranda and address her husband

Mother Mole-Cricket Well, all I can say is that it serves you right. It's no good coming to me for sympathy, you've brought all this upon yourself! (*She makes a further brisk sweep with the broom before leaning it against the door and crossing down into the garden*) If you had taken the trouble to listen to me in the first place, you wouldn't be in this position now. It's all this messing about with astrology and telescopes and things that don't concern you.

Father Mole-Cricket groans and turns away

But this much I will tell you: if you bring shame on this house by being publicly executed I shall never speak to you again. Royal Acting Unpaid Astrologer indeed! Such nonsense!

Father Mole-Cricket (*rising*) How was I to know that all this would happen?

Mother Mole-Cricket I said from the very beginning that no good would come of it. After all, if you decide to take all this interest in what goes on in the heavens, you can't start complaining when you're given the opportunity of a closer look. If you should chance to travel in that direction.

Father Mole-Cricket groans again

Master Mole-Cricket (*crossing down*) I wonder what time they'll come to take you away, Father?

Father Mole-Cricket I wish you'd both stop talking about it. It's bad enough as it is, without the pair of you going on and on and on ...

Master Mole-Cricket I expect they'll do it at dawn tomorrow. It usually happens at dawn. Dawn! What a terrible time to have to get out of bed!

Father Mole-Cricket It would serve you right if they chopped off your head as well. Don't forget, you are my assistant, you know.

Master Mole-Cricket You don't think they will, do you, Father?

Father Mole-Cricket I don't see why not.

Mother Mole-Cricket It's no more or less than either of you deserve. I only hope it teaches you both a lesson.

Master Mole-Cricket I shouldn't think they will bother with me, really. The Emperor will probably be quite satisfied with your head, Father.

Father Mole-Cricket groans again

Never mind. Cheer up. I have heard that you can have just what you like for breakfast on the last morning.

Father Mole-Cricket I don't suppose I shall feel like eating.

Master Mole-Cricket I'll come along with you, if you like, and give you a hand with what's left over.

Mother Mole-Cricket You'll do nothing of the kind. (*She returns to the veranda*) You'll bring it straight back here for the chickens.

Father Mole-Cricket You might, at least, wait until I'm dead before you start sharing out my breakfast.

Mother Mole-Cricket It's all very well for you, you'll have nothing to worry about, but it's no easy life being a widow these days. After all, you don't want to leave this world with the thought that you've left a starving wife and child behind.

Father Mole-Cricket I don't want to leave this world under any circumstances. I wish you'd leave me alone. I want to think.

Mother Mole-Cricket If you want my advice, the best thing you can do is get some work done to take your mind off things. There is the wood to be chopped.

Father Mole-Cricket And stop talking about chopping!

Mother Mole-Cricket Well, if all you're going to do is sit and sulk in the garden, I,

for one, have no time to stand and watch you. I've plenty of things on my mind
without troubling myself with your worries.

Mother Mole-Cricket flounces off into the house

Master Mole-Cricket She's quite right, you know, Father. It's not a bit of use
worrying about it now. (*He yawns*) We might just as well wait and let things happen
of their own accord ... And while we are waiting—we might just as well be resting.
(*He lies down on the grass*) I ... I do feel rather sleepy ... It's all this fuss and bother,
I think ... (*He is fast asleep*)
Father Mole-Cricket A fine family I've got! Resting indeed! As if I could possibly
rest with the thought of all this in my head. (*He feels his head gingerly*) By this
time tomorrow I won't have a head. (*He crosses and sits on the veranda steps*)
Who would have thought that four days could have flown so quickly? Four days!
As if I could possibly have found four thieves in four days! And it's Friday already
... Four days. One—two—three—four. Tuesday—Wednesday—Thursday—Friday.
One—two—three—four. As for the thieves, they're probably miles away by now.
One thing's certain, at least—they certainly aren't likely to come anywhere near
this village ...

As he speaks the four Thieves creep on R, *in a sinister manner. The leader of the
thieves looks all around and then motions his men to follow him across the garden*

Four days! What chance have I had? One ...

The Leader of the Thieves trots across the garden

Two ...

The First Thief trots across the garden

Three ...

The Second Thief trots across the garden

Four ...

The Third Thief trots across the garden

One—two—three—four ...

There is general consternation among the Thieves

First Thief Here! I can hear someone counting us!
Second Thief So can I!
Third Thief Me too!
Leader Will you be quiet! (*He peers around the garden and sees the sign*) Mercy on us! Why this is the house of Father Mole-Cricket, the astrologer! We are discovered!
First Thief Finished!
Third Thief That must be him over there!
Second Thief Listen! He's speaking again!
Leader Hush!
Father Mole-Cricket I know just what's going to happen. The Emperor is going to expect me to say, (*loudly*) "I know who the thieves are, your Majesty. I know their names. I know all about them, I can arrest them whenever I like."

There is consternation among the Thieves

First Thief Indera Maya will have us hung!
Second Thief Hanged. And drawn!
Third Thief And quartered!
Leader Indera Maya will certainly have us hung ...
Second Thief Hanged.
Leader I'm sorry. Hanged—and drawn and quartered.
Third Thief He might have pity on me. I only took the smallest chest.
First Thief That was because you couldn't carry a larger one. You're just as bad as the rest of us.
Third Thief I'm not then!
First Thief You are then!
Third Thief Not then!
First Thief Are then!
Leader Be quiet both of you! We are all as bad as one another. Neither more nor less than downright criminals. There is only one thing we can do. We must give ourselves up.
First Thief Oh, no! If we give ourselves up we shall be whipped!
Second Thief If we give ourselves up we shall be beaten!
Third Thief If we give ourselves up we shall be flogged!
Leader If you don't do as I say, I shall whip and beat and flog you all myself.
First Thief I vote we give ourselves up.
Second Thief Hear, hear!
Leader Good. Then we are all agreed. Come along, we must give ourselves up to Father Mole-Cricket.

The four Thieves approach the veranda

Good-morning, Father Mole-Cricket!

Father Mole-Cricket looks up. Master Mole-Cricket wakes, yawns, stretches himself and rises

Father Mole-Cricket Good-morning, gentlemen. Did you wish to see me?
Leader We have come to give ourselves up.
Father Mole-Cricket To what?
Leader To give ourselves up.
Father Mole-Cricket You'd better find a Royal Policeman, I'm far too busy at the moment.
Leader But we want to give ourselves up to you, Father Mole-Cricket.
First Thief And we promise we will never do it again.
Second Thief Never as long as we live.
Third Thief I only took the smallest chest, Father Mole-Cricket. It was so small I was sure that his Majesty would never notice it was missing.

The Leader of the Thieves pushes the Third Thief aside, impatiently

Father Mole-Cricket (*rising*) Excuse me, did you say "chest"?
Third Thief *Smallest* chest, Father Mole-Cricket. The very smallest chest there was. I wouldn't have taken it otherwise.
Leader (*again brushing the Third Thief aside*) Will you be quiet! We should have known that you would have discovered us, Father Mole-Cricket.
Father Mole-Cricket (*crossing down into garden*) Oh yes! You should have known that. Did you hear that my boy! "Chests", they said!
Master Mole-Cricket I did indeed, Father.
Leader If we had given the matter our careful consideration, Father Mole-Cricket, we would never have, er ... borrowed the chests.
Father Mole-Cricket No, I'm sure you wouldn't. Four chests, wasn't it?
Leader That's right.
Third Thief Three large chests, Father Mole-Cricket, and one very small one. You will remember that I did mention the small one was the one I took.
Leader (*again pushing the Third Thief aside*) Four chests, Father Mole-Cricket.
Father Mole-Cricket Well, well, well! Four chests, eh? Did you hear that, my boy?
Master Mole-Cricket Indeed I did, Father.
Father Mole-Cricket From his Majesty's Royal Vaults, would it be?
Leader Yes, yes. That's right. And now we have come to give ourselves up.
Father Mole-Cricket Have you now? You know, that was a very wise thing to do. Very wise.
Leader What will become of us, Father Mole-Cricket?
First Thief Will we be hung?
Second Thief Hanged. And drawn?
Third Thief And quartered?
Father Mole-Cricket Every bit of it, I should imagine. And a great deal more than that, I shouldn't wonder.

Leader Isn't there anything we can do?

Father Mole-Cricket Well ... Yes, possibly there is. But first, you must do two things for me.

Second Thief We shall be only too pleased, Father Mole-Cricket, to help you in any way we can.

Leader No matter how great or small, we are yours to command.

Father Mole-Cricket Then first, you must promise that you won't be caught stealing again.

Leader We shall never be *caught* stealing again, Father Mole-Cricket.

First Thief We wouldn't think of it, Father Mole-Cricket.

Second Thief We wouldn't even consider any such similar malpractice.

Third Thief Not even the tiniest chest you could ever imagine. Even smaller than the one I took, that was very, very small indeed.

Leader The errors of all our past misdeeds lie heavy on all our unhappy hearts.

Father Mole-Cricket Good. And, secondly you must tell me what you have done with the four chests of gold.

Leader You'll let us go free?

First Thief And we won't be hung—hanged?

Second Thief Or drawn?

Third Thief Not even quartered?

Father Mole-Cricket Not if you tell me what I want to know. I could, of course, easily look it up in the stars, you know. But if you care to confess it will save me the trouble of finding my spectacles. And you shall go free. But if I ever do study the stars and discover that you've been thieving again, I shall have no mercy whatsoever.

Leader I call for a general conference!

The four Thieves huddle together for a brief muttered conference. As they reach an agreement the Leader of the Thieves crosses to Father Mole-Cricket

We agree.

Father Mole-Cricket And the chests?

Leader We lost them, Father Mole-Cricket.

Father Mole-Cricket Lost them!

First Thief In a way.

Second Thief More or less.

Third Thief Generally speaking.

Leader Only this morning.

Second Thief Not more than an hour ago.

First Thief If that.

Third Thief Probably less.

Father Mole-Cricket Lost them!

Leader This is the way it was: you see, we chanced to call at an inn.

First Thief Not far from here.

Second Thief Just down the road.

Third Thief That's just what we did.

Leader And while we were there we met some sailors.

First Thief Very friendly they were.

Second Thief Or so we thought.

Third Thief That's how it seemed.

Leader Giving us drinks.

First Thief Plenty of money.

Second Thief Pockets were bulging.

Third Thief Oh, very nice men.

Leader What else could we think?

Father Mole-Cricket Go on ...

Leader We were wrong. Rogues, they were, every one of them.

First Thief Robbers.

Second Thief Tricksters.

Third Thief Thieves.

Leader People like them deserve to be locked up.

Father Mole-Cricket What happened?

Leader One of them, the Captain I took him to be, by the way the others was a-speaking, suggests we play a game of cards. Well, like, it seems a harmless suggestion. A game of cards. As good a way to pass the time as any—us being sort of unemployed for the morning. Mostly we work nights, you see. So—off we goes. Believe it or not, Father Mole-Cricket, within the hour we'd lost every penny we possessed. Gambling, you know. It's been the downfall of many a respectable criminal.

Father Mole-Cricket You lost the gold?

Leader Every single piece.

Third Thief Even the smallest chest, Father Mole-Cricket, which you may recall I ...

He is pushed aside by the leader of the Thieves

Father Mole-Cricket And the sailors? Are they still at this inn?

Leader (*shaking his head sadly*) No, no. That's the unhappy ending, as you might say. They upped and off with the chests of gold leaving us to pay for the drinks

First Thief We had to pick the landlord's pocket.

Leader Said they had a tide to catch. A likely story.

Father Mole-Cricket You didn't by any chance, overhear the name of their ship?

Leader No, no. Unhappily not. But wait—I did get this. (*He takes a gold watch and chain from his pocket*) Whilst in the process of bending down to fasten my shoe-lace, my hand, inadvertently, strayed past the Captain's jacket. Somehow or other, my fingers seemed to get caught up in the chain. I can't think how it happened. Imagine my surprise when, not two minutes ago, I found the article still to be in my possession. His watch, I think. (*He passes the watch to Father Mole-Cricket*) Gold all through. Eighteen carat. There's an inscription inside.

Father Mole-Cricket (*opening and reading the watch-case*) "Captain Beanfeast, Master of the *Bold Tassel!*"

Leader I suppose that might be the name you're seeking. There's also a motto in smaller writing. "Honesty is the best policy." What a lovely thought!

Father Mole-Cricket absent-mindedly closes the watch and puts it in his pocket

Thanks very much.

Father Mole-Cricket (*returning the watch*) I beg your pardon.

The three thieves make a concerted grab for the watch but the Leader brushes them aside

Leader I quite understand. (*He returns the watch to his pocket*) Well, if that's all the information you require, Father Mole-Cricket you did say ...

Father Mole-Cricket Yes, that's all. Now, just you listen to me. I've decided to be lenient with you—this time. But whether the Emperor would feel the same way I wouldn't care to say. And so, if I were you, I should get out of here as quickly as you can and start running, and I shouldn't stop running until I came to ...

The four Thieves have already taken his advice and exited

Goodness me! They've gone!

Master Mole-Cricket What are you going to do now, Father?

Father Mole-Cricket *We*, my boy, are going to run away to sea.

Master Mole-Cricket But it's far too warm to run anywhere this morning!

Father Mole-Cricket It's our only chance. We must get down to the harbour ourselves, and climb aboard as quickly as we can. We must return with those four chests of gold, my son.

Master Mole-Cricket That's all very well, Father. But I still don't see why I have to go with you. I am feeling rather tired this morning and ...

Father Mole-Cricket You don't have to go with me, my boy. But remember, if the Emperor calls to chop off my head and my head isn't here to be chopped, he may very well lose his temper. He may even decide to chop off someone else's head instead. Yours, for instance. After all—you are the Assistant Acting Unpaid Royal Astrologer.

Master Mole-Cricket Now I see why I have to go with you.

Father Mole-Cricket Besides, when you say that you are going to run away to sea, it doesn't mean that you are going to run anywhere. It's merely a figure of speech.

Master Mole-Cricket Then what does it mean?

Father Mole-Cricket Simply, that you go down to the harbour and stow away.

Master Mole-Cricket Stow away?

Father Mole-Cricket Which means that you find a nice comfortable place to hide on board a ship. And then you go to sleep until someone comes along and finds you.

Master Mole-Cricket Nice comfortable place? Go to sleep? I think that running away to sea sounds like one of the best ideas you ever had! But we'd better do it quickly ... because ... (*he yawns*) because, I'm beginning to feel very ... very ... sleepy ...

Father Mole-Cricket Of course, there is your mother to consider. We'd better tell her ... No, wait! Perhaps we'd better not. She'd be sure to find some work for us to do before we went. I have it! We'll leave her a note ... (*He fumbles through his pockets and takes out a pencil and paper*) You bring me my telescope, my boy, we may need it.

Master Mole-Cricket collects the telescope from the veranda as his father writes the note

Dear wife ... We have found the Emperor's chests of gold. We must go to sea at once. ... There!

Master Mole-Cricket hands the telescope to his father

Thank you, son. And now, where can we leave this? ... The very place! (*He crosses to the sign and sticks the note on a jutting nail*) Your mother is sure to see it there. And now! Ready, my boy?

Master Mole-Cricket I'm ready, Father.

Father Mole-Cricket Then off we go! (*He points, off, with the telescope*) To sea! Come along, my boy! We must hurry!

Master Mole-Cricket (*yawning*) Coming, Father. ... I'm coming!

Father Mole-Cricket exits L

Master Mole-Cricket yawns, stretches and trudges off L

A short pause before the Emperor enters R

Emperor Come along, Chancellor! Come along, man!

A weary Chancellor enters R

Chancellor Coming, Majesty ... I'm coming ...

Emperor Goodness me, Chancellor! One of these days you'll be late for your own execution.

Chancellor (*sighing and sitting on the grass*) If I may be allowed to rest a moment, Majesty. ...

Emperor Rest? Rest! We can't rest now, Chancellor! We have business to attend to. This man Cratchitt.

Chancellor The name is Cricket, Majesty. Mole-Cricket.

Emperor Never mind what the name is, Chancellor. Where is he? Why isn't he here? He knows perfectly well that he has to be executed. The four days are over, aren't they?

Chancellor They are indeed, Majesty.

Emperor Well then, why isn't he here? The executioner will be arriving from the Palace at any minute with his wicket and we've no Hatchet—hatchet and we've no Wicket.

Chancellor Cricket, Majesty.

Emperor Same game. Where is he? This is his house, isn't it?

Chancellor Indeed it is, Majesty. His name is on the board over there.

Emperor (*crossing to the sign*) Board? ... Board? ... (*He takes down the note*) Why! Bless my soul! ... Chancellor, listen to this! "Dear wife. We have found the Emperor's chests of gold. We must go to sea at once!" Chancellor, he's gone to sea!

Chancellor (*still examining his aching feet*) To see what, Majesty?

Emperor To sea in a ship, you nincompoop! He's stolen my chests of gold and gone to sea! Him and that son of his. To think that that boy was to marry my daughter! A common thief. Just wait until I get my hands on them. The fleet, Chancellor! That's the answer. We'll put to sea in the Royal Fleet—bring them back—and then, Chancellor, and then ... (*He draws his finger across his throat*) On your feet, man! Up! Up! Chin in, chest out! We must get down to the harbour at once.

The Chancellor climbs unhappily to his feet

Wait a minute! Take a message! Pencil! Paper!

The Chancellor takes his notebook and pencil from his robes

We must leave a note for the Royal Executioner. Ready?

The Chancellor inclines his head

Then put this: "Bring the axe to the harbour. We'll do it there." Got that? Good.

The Chancellor tears out the page and hands it to the Emperor who fixes it on the nail on the sign

There! Now, Chancellor! To the harbour! Quick march! To the sea! Joy, joy, joy! I do love ships!

The Emperor hurries off L

The Chancellor moves as if to follow him, hesitates and addresses the audience

Chancellor One of these days I'm going to tell that man exactly what I think of him. Emperor or no Emperor. And it won't be very pleasant. I don't mind telling you. All right, let him chop off my head. At least I'll have had the satisfaction of knowing that I've told him the truth, for once. "Emperor," I shall say, "Emperor, I have only one thing to say to you, and it's this ... "
Emperor (*off*) Chancellor! ... Chancellor!!
Chancellor Coming, Majesty! I'm coming.

He turns to the audience as if to speak again, changes his mind, sighs and limps off L

The door at the rear opens and Mother Mole-Cricket enters. She carries a bundle of firewood and a small hatchet

Mother Mole-Cricket (*calling from the veranda*) Husband! Idler! Good-for-nothing! Come here at once and chop this wood! (*She crosses down into the garden and looks around*) It's no use hiding! The work must be done! (*She sees the note on the sign, glances down at the hatchet*) "Bring the axe to the harbour. We'll do it there." We'll do nothing of the kind! (*She puts the bundle of wood on the ground and sits on it*) We'll do it right here—or not at all!

She is patiently waiting for her missing husband as the Lights fade

QUEST FOR THE WHOOPERDINK
by A.H. Teacey

There are two extracts from this play, the first from Act I and the second from Act II. They may be performed as separate pieces or run together as one.

In the first scene Professor Potterton, a 'character' scientist, and his daughter, Crystal, have set out in search of the rare Whooperdink bird in Urgleland, when they arrive at the Fiery Cave. But the wicked witch and her son, Seth, who is under a spell of idiocy, also wish to find this bird.

Set: Outside the Fiery Cave, a passage between two strange lands, with the cave's entrance upstage.
This play was conceived for theatre-in-the-round, but may be staged in other ways.

Cast: M3 F2.
Professor Potterton, a scientist, whose two chief attributes are a keen enthusiasm and an ability to become totally absorbed in whatever has taken his attention. Crystal, his daughter, attractive both physically and by nature. The Guardian of the Fiery Cave, a godlike figure of awe. Salmonella, the wicked witch. Seth, her 21-year-old son, who is under a spell and appears simple.

Playing time: 11 minutes.

Outside the Fiery Cave

The Fiery Cave is a passage between two strange lands. The cave's entrance is UL *and its exit is* UR. *There is a large rock* UR *close by the exit*

The Lights come up on Crystal who enters wearily DL, *carrying her bag. She stops and looks around*

Crystal (*calling over her shoulder*) Come on, Father!
Professor (*off*) Just a minute, dear, I'm just looking at——
Professor } (*together*) { (*off; excitedly*)
Crystal } { (*wearily*) —another rock!

Crystal Father, we'll never get there at this rate.

The Professor enters DL, *carrying a bag and a rock*

Professor (*as he enters*) Absolutely splendid! I've never seen rocks like these before. Open the bag, dear; I'll just put a label on it and pop it in with the others.
Crystal Can't we stop and have something to eat now? Where are we anyway?

She looks at the map whilst the Professor continues to examine rocks

(*Looking at the cave entrance* UL) Oh, this must be——

The Guardian of the Fiery Cave suddenly appears at the entrance UL. *He carries two fire stones*

Crystal stands and stares at the Guardian. The Professor, oblivious, continues to search for more specimens DR

Professor What have we here? This seems to be——
Crystal Father. Father!

The Professor turns and sees the Guardian. He too is awe-struck

Guardian I am the Guardian of the Fiery Cave. I have been here since time began, and my sole purpose is to guard the passage through the Fiery Cave. None may pass this way, save those who satisfy the Test of the Flames.
Professor Oh, I say, is this your cave? Those stalagmites look absolutely splendid, fascinating. Could I just——?

The Professor goes to enter the cave UL *but the Guardian bars his way*

Guardian None may pass this way, save those who satisfy the Test of the Flames.
Crystal Father!

The Professor and Crystal settle down to listen

Guardian The test is this: you must each take a fire stone and cast it into the cave. The stone will reveal whether you are good or evil. Only the good may pass. If the stone flares red, this shows you to be good, and you may proceed. If the stone flares green, then you are evil, and will be cast into the cave to feed the fiery flames. Do you wish to take the test?
Crystal We are good people, aren't we, Father?
Professor I think so, basically ... though once ...
Crystal (*anxiously*) What?
Professor Well ... once I took Henry Davidson's Aesculus Hippocastanum fruit.

Crystal What's that?
Professor What?
Crystal An Aescle ... Hippo ...?
Professor Aesculus Hippocastanum? A Horse-Chestnut, of course.
Crystal A Horse-Chestnut fruit—you mean a conker?
Professor Yes, that's right.
Crystal When was that?
Professor Oh, when I was—eight.
Crystal I don't think that counts.
Guardian Do you wish to take the test?
Professor (*to Crystal*) We must go this way, mustn't we?

Crystal nods

Well, I suppose so, yes.
Guardian (*holding out the fire stones*) These are the fire stones.
Professor Oh, I say ...! (*He stands up and takes a stone*)
Crystal (*standing*) Father!
Professor Absolutely astounding! I have never seen alumina oxide fused with mica schist like this before. Fascinating!
Guardian Cast the stone.

The Professor does not want to let go of this unique specimen

Cast the stone.
Professor Er—you wouldn't happen to have a spare one I could take with me as a specimen——?
Guardian CAST THE STONE!

The Professor shrugs and casts the stone into the cave entrance UL. *It flares red*

Professor Amazing! That must be caused by the alumina's metamorphosis——
Guardian Pass!
Professor But Crystal——
Guardian PASS!
Professor Oh well ...

The Professor picks up his bag and exits into the cave entrance UL

Guardian (*handing Crystal the other stone*) Cast the stone.

Crystal takes it, closes her eyes, crosses her fingers and throws it into the Cave entrance UL. *It flares red*

Pass.

Crystal Thank you.

Crystal picks up her bag and follows her father into the cave entrance UL. *The Guardian exits* UL

The Lights change to suggest a new landscape at the other end of the cave. Pause

The Professor enters from the cave UR. *After a pause, Crystal enters from* UR, *following her father*

Professor Ah. There you are!
Crystal Which way now, Father?
Professor Oh, let me see ... this way, I think ...

The Professor and Crystal exit DR

The Lights return to normal as they were at the beginning of the scene

Salmonella and Seth enter DL *and approach the cave entrance* UL. *Salmonella carries her magic bag and Seth carries the haversack*

Salmonella Aaahhh ... Hssssss!
Seth What's up?
Salmonella I was watching the Professor and his daughter at the Fiery Cave, and I don't like what I saw.
Seth What did you see, Mam?
Salmonella To get through that cave, we have to pass a test.
Seth I don't think I can pass a test.
Salmonella I don't think I can pass this one, either. Unless ... (*She reaches for her magic book*) I'll have to use some magic. (*Consulting the book*) "Spell For Changing Things" ... Hmmmm (*reading*):
>   "When you need to make things seem
>   Other than the things they've been,
>   Use your Magic Aerosol ..."

(*She bends down and takes the aerosol out of her bag*)

>   "And say the word 'Batfoldirol'
>   And if your spell is carefully made,
>   Those things will change which you have sprayed."

(*She chooses two stones from those lying around and places them* C. *She then casts the spell—not forgetting "Batfoldirol"—circling the stones as she does so*)

"Now when these stones to fire are fed,
Make them flare, and make them red!"

Yesss ... that should do nicely, hehehehehehehe. (*She puts the stones in her bag*) Seth, come here. Stand still. Stop fidgeting. (*She slaps him*) Now listen very carefully. When we go into that cave, a man will give you a stone.

Seth Why?

Salmonella So that you can throw it into the cave.

Seth Why does he give me a stone just for me to throw it away?

Salmonella Well ... it's a kind of game.

Seth A birthday game?

Salmonella Yes—if you like, a birthday game.

Seth Ooh, goody! What happens next?

Salmonella Well, although he wants you to throw it away——

Seth Yes?

Salmonella — it's a trick. If you throw it away, you lose!

Seth Ooh!

Salmonella Instead, if you are to win the game——

Seth Yes?

Salmonella —you must throw a different stone away.

Seth Oh.

Salmonella One that I've hidden in my bag.

Seth Yes! Yes! Yes! (*Singing*) It's a birthday game, a birthday game——

Salmonella (*thumping him*) Be quiet and listen!

Seth Yes, Mam.

Salmonella When he asks you——

Seth Who?

Salmonella The man in the cave——

Seth Yes!

Salmonella When he asks you to throw it away——

Seth Yes!

Salmonella Don't throw it away——

Seth No!

Salmonella Get rid of it——

Seth Yes! Where?

Salmonella Anywhere—your pocket—anywhere!

Seth Yes!

Salmonella Then I'll give you another stone from this bag. (*She points to the stones in her bag*)

Seth But there are ... two stones there.

Salmonella Right! One for each of us.

Seth Are you going to play, too?

Salmonella Yes.

Seth Ohhh, goodygoodygoody——

Salmonella So—I'll give you another stone, from this bag——
Seth Yes!
Salmonella And then——
Seth I put that in my pocket, too!
Salmonella No! (*She thumps him*) You throw that away.
Seth (*after a pause*) Throw it away? But you said I hadn't to throw it away!
Salmonella That was the first stone! (*Pointing into the bag*) This is the second stone. Throw this one away.
Seth (*still looking into the bag*) Mam, which of these is the second stone?
Salmonella Oh, idiot, they're *both* second stones.
Seth (*totally confused*) Both second stones?
Salmonella Listen. (*After a pause*) The man in the cave will give you a stone. Put it in your pocket——
Seth In my pocket.
Salmonella Or throw it away, get rid of it.
Seth Throw it away.
Salmonella Then you get a second stone from this bag, and you throw that one into the cave.
Seth Into the cave.
Salmonella Now, have you got that?

They look at each other for a moment. Seth is about to reply as:

The Guardian appears UL *from the cave entrance. He carries two fire stones*

Oh, never mind, just do as I say.
Seth Yes, Mam. (*To the Guardian*) Hallo. I've come to play your game!
Guardian I am the Guardian of the Fiery Cave.
Seth (*after a pause*) Are you going to talk to him, Mam?

Pause

I think he wants to talk, Mam.

Pause. The Guardian folds his arms

(*Rushing to hide behind Salmonella*) I don't think I like him, Mam!
Guardian I am the Guardian of the Fiery Cave. I have been here since time began, and my sole purpose is to guard the passage through the Fiery Cave. None may pass this way, save those who satisfy the Test of the Flames. Do you know about the test?
Seth Yes. My mam's just told——

Salmonella stamps on Seth's foot

Ooowwwww! Mam!

Salmonella No.

Guardian The test is this: you must each take a fire stone and cast it into the cave. The stone will reveal whether you are good or evil. Only the good may pass. If the stone flares red, this shows you to be good, and you may proceed. If the stone flares green, then you are evil, and will be cast into the cave, to feed the fiery flames. Do you wish to take the test?

Seth No—I'm not very good at tests!

Salmonella (*thumping him*) Yes!

Guardian (*to Seth*) Take the stone.

Seth takes the stone from the Guardian

Salmonella (*whispering to Seth*) Now get rid of it.

Seth (*confused and frightened*) Now? Where?

Salmonella Anywhere! But not——

Seth throws the stone into the cave UL

—into the cave!

The stone flares red

Red? That flare was red ...

Guardian Pass.

Seth Mam ...?

Guardian Pass!

Seth shrugs, picks up his haversack and the magic bag containing the two false stones and starts to go into the cave entrance UL

(*To Salmonella*) Take the stone.

She realizes that the false stones are in her bag, which Seth has taken

Salmonella (*hesitating*) Erm ... Er ... Ssss!

Seth realizes he has the bag containing the false stones and stops, just visible inside the cave entrance

Seth (*turning back*) Mam! (*He bends down and takes a false stone from the bag*) Mam, your stone ...

Salmonella acts quickly. She grabs the stone from the Guardian and throws it to Seth. Seth catches this stone, but in so doing drops his own false stone which flares red. The Guardian sees this and takes it to be the stone thrown by Salmonella

Guardian Pass.

Salmonella joins Seth inside the cave entrance UL *and they move out of sight. Pause. The Guardian follows them into the cave* UL

The Lights change as before to suggest the new landscape at the other end of the cave

Salmonella and Seth appear from the cave UR

Seth What shall we do with this stone?
Salmonella (*cackling with delight*) Hehehehehe ... give it to me.
                     If evil through and through I've been,
                     No doubt this true stone will flare green!

On the last word Salmonella throws the stone in the cave UR *and there is a tremendous green flare from within the cave*

   Hehehehehe!
Seth What now, Mam?
Salmonella We must follow the Professor and his daughter, of course.
Seth Why, Mam?
Salmonella (*exasperated*) Because they will lead us to the Whooperdink! (*She pauses*) Wait a minute. You've given me an idea. Why are we following them? Why don't we join them? Why not make it a party of four?
Seth A birthday party?
Salmonella Shhh! I'm thinking. If I could persuade the Professor that I too was a scientist out on an expedition——
Seth What's an exposition, Mam?
Salmonella —he might let us join him, and that would save all the fuss and bother of trying to follow him. Yesss. We'll do that. But first, I must change my clothes. Come, son!
Seth Will there be sweets at this party, Mam?

Salmonella and Seth exit DR

The Lights fade to Black-out

In the final scene of the play, Seth has been magically cured, and he and Crystal return, under Urgle guard, to the Snowy Plains, where the Snowflake Maker helps sort out their problems.

Set: The Snowy Plains.

Cast: M3 F2, 3M or F.
In the second scene also appear the following: The Snowflake Maker, an elderly Cockney, whose melancholic exterior hides a heart of gold. Two Urgles, other-worldly, timid but quick-moving creatures. The Whooperdink, a bird with blue and purple body, yellow beak, legs and tail feathers, vulnerable and instantly lovable. Salmonella becomes a typically nice mum named Marcia in this scene.

Playing time: 13 minutes.

The Snowy Plains

A snowflake lighting effect comes up on the Snowflake Maker who is sitting in his deckchair c, *reading his brochures*

Crystal, Seth and the Urgles enter DR

Crystal There he is.

The Lights come up to full

The Snowflake Maker. (*To the Snowflake Maker*) Hallo!
Snowflake Maker My goodness me! Well, well, well, if it isn't our Crystal and——
Crystal Seth.
Snowflake Maker Seth, yes. But I don't recognize your other friends. They're not Mum and Dad in disguise, are they?
Crystal (*smiling*) No. We've brought you something. Look. (*She shows him the magic snowflake*)
Snowflake Maker Blimey! (*He stands, and is mesmerized by it*) I can't believe me eyes. It's a magic snowflake. Is it really? I never thought I'd see the day—can I?
Crystal Of course. (*She hands it to him*)
Snowflake Maker Oh my giddy aunt ... ain't it beautiful. I can't believe it! At last I can have me wish. Oh thank you, thank you, me dear. (*He stands up and hugs and kisses Crystal*)

Crystal Well it was Seth who found it really.

Snowflake Maker (*likewise hugging and kissing Seth*) Oh thank you, thank you! Oh, I'm so excited. Where shall I go? (*He reaches for a brochure*) Which sandy beach shall I choose?

Crystal Well ... we were wondering ...

Snowflake Maker Yes? You know somewhere nice? I'll go there. If you recommend it, it must be good.

Crystal No, listen, please.

Snowflake Maker What?

Crystal (*after a pause*) My dad and his mum have gone to find the Whooperdink, and we're trying to find them. Is there any chance you might use this magic snowflake to bring them all back?

Snowflake Maker What? (*To Seth*) Your mum? That green-faced old goat? No chance.

Crystal Please.

Snowflake Maker NO.

Seth Please.

Snowflake Maker Never in a million years, son. Never in a million, billion, trillion years! You don't know how long I've waited for this. I owes it to all Snowflake Makers, my father——

Crystal But you don't know how much my father means to me. I want him back safe and sound. I love him.

Snowflake Maker (*softening*) Yes, but ...

Seth And there's my mum, too.

Snowflake Maker That grizzly green-faced grouser! No, me mind's made up! (*He is about to throw the magic snowflake*)

The Professor, the Whooperdink and Salmonella enter UL

Professor Crystal!

Crystal (*running to the Professor and hugging him*) Dad, oh Dad! I'm so glad you're safe!

Salmonella Seth, is that you?

Seth It is, yes.

Salmonella Seth? You sound different.

Seth I'm not stupid any more, Mum. The spell has been broken.

Salmonella What is four times four?

Seth Sixteen.

Salmonella What do you like to eat?

Seth Swee——Chocolates.

Salmonella How many p's in poppy?

Seth Three, Mum.

Salmonella Ha—there's only—oh yes, three. You're right. You have changed. How?

Seth It's a long story, Mum.
Salmonella I'm waiting.
Seth Well, remember the last lines of the curse—"A whoop, a cry"?
Salmonella Yes.
Seth The whoop was the Whooperdink's magic, and the cry——

Seth holds out his hand to Crystal who moves towards him

—the cry was Crystal's tears.
Salmonella Crysssstal! Yes, go on.
Seth And "the brush so light"—that was a feather Crystal gave me as my birthday present. I used it to brush away her tears.
Salmonella A feather?
Seth Yes, the Whooperdink's feathers are magic——
Crystal (*aghast*) SETH!
Salmonella Aha!

The secret is out, and, whilst Seth holds his head in shame and horror, Salmonella grabs the Whooperdink once again

Now, at last, I shall be the greatest witch! All powerful! I shall turn this land of snow into freezing ice! You think you've been cold? You don't know what cold is, yet! Sssss! (*To the Professor*) You. You interfering old intellectual, with your precious rocks. I shall turn you into solid rock, and you shall stay buried beneath the ice for ever and ever! (*To Seth*) I've had to put up with your stupidity for twenty years. And now that the curse is lifted, you're none the wiser! I can see what you feel for her. You think her spell over you is stronger than any of mine? Ha! Well, think again! I could have made you great, now that the curse has gone. You could have flown with me, been my greatest familiar! But now—since you love her, you can stay with her and share her fate! (*To Crystal*) As for you ... you will never touch or see him again. Your heart will be the start, and from there you will turn into a solid lump of ice. You will go colder and colder, and as you freeze, your feet will stick to the ground and you will never be heard of or seen again! Now, with this feather——(*She reaches for one of the Whooperdink's feathers*)
Snowflake Maker NO!

The Snowflake Maker throws the magic snowflake at the witch. She is showered in magic snow, and freezes instantly. There is a stunned silence

Professor What happened?
Crystal You used it! You did it after all! You used your only chance to stop the witch.
Snowflake Maker Yes.

Crystal runs to the Snowflake Maker and hugs and kisses him. Seth does likewise

Crystal But what about you now? You've stopped the witch, and she can't harm the Whooperdink, and that's marvellous. But you've lost your chance to get away.
Snowflake Maker Yes. Yes, I have, haven't I?
Crystal Oh, what a shame. You've waited such a long time, (*she starts to cry*) dreamed about it for so long. (*She cries*)
Snowflake Maker I don't care.
Crystal What?
Snowflake Maker Really, it doesn't matter now. I've seen it, I've held it, and I've used it. Used it to help you. (*He sniffs*) And do you know, I've never felt happier!
Seth But your dreams, the sunshine ...?
Snowflake Maker Well, I've still got me dreams, ain't I? And me brochures. But for once in my life I've been able to do something useful, to help somebody. And no sun could make me feel warmer inside than I am now.
Crystal (*crying*) Oh, Mr Snowflake Maker.

Crystal and the Snowflake Maker have a good cry together

Professor My goodness! Good gracious! (*He bends down to the feet of the Snowflake Maker and Crystal*) Whatever can these be?
Seth (*bending down*) Your tears. They've become——
Seth
Crystal } (*together*)—magic snowflakes!
Snowflake Maker Magic snowflakes!
Seth One ... two ... three. (*To the Snowflake Maker*) Look. Take them, they're yours.
Snowflake Maker But how? Why?
Seth I don't really know—but I think it's something to do with crying for the right reasons.
Professor Well, whatever the reason, Mr Snowflake Maker has three more of these ...
Crystal Magic snowflakes!
Professor Yes, three more magic snowflakes to use. What are you going to do with them?

The Urgles step forward, and indicate that they would like their Whooperdink back

1st Urgle Urgle Whooperdink urgle!
2nd Urgle Urgle!
Professor Oh, I think they want their Whooperdink back. (*To the 1st Urgle*) Urgle Whooperdink urgle?
1st Urgle
2nd Urgle } (*together, nodding*) Urgle.
Crystal Well, we did promise, didn't we?

Seth Yes, we did.

Professor Yes, of course. (*After a pause*) Only ...

Crystal What?

Professor Well, we've come all this way on the quest for the Whooperdink, and here it is. And now they're going to take it away from me, and I'll probably never see it again. Oh, botheration! So near, and yet so far. If only I had some evidence. A photograph. But I haven't brought my camera. Oh, I wish I had a camera!

Snowflake Maker Then you shall have one.

Professor But——

Snowflake Maker I can wish one for you!

Crystal Would you really?

Snowflake Maker Of course I would. Oooh, I haven't had so much fun in—in— ever! Stand back! (*He puts two magic snowflakes down, and prepares to throw the third*)

Professor Erm ... could you make it a Polaroid 2000, please?

Snowflake Maker One Polaroid 2000 coming up!

Professor Thank you so much.

The Snowflake Maker throws the magic snowflake at the Professor's bag

Crystal (*fetching the bag*) Look in the bag, Father.

Professor Oooh, isn't this exciting. I can hardly bear to look. (*He looks in the bag; there is a squeal of delight*) It is, it is! A Polaroid 2000! Splendid, absolutely! (*To Crystal*) Would you, please ...?

The Professor gives the camera to Crystal and he poses alongside the Whooperdink. Crystal takes a photograph and everyone gathers around to look at it. (It is possible to load a Polaroid 2000 with a previously-taken photograph, thus allowing for really "instant" photographs.) The Urgles "ask" to see it, and indicate that they would like a photograph taken, too. Crystal takes a photograph of the Professor, the Whooperdink and the two Urgles

Crystal Smile! Urgle!

The Urgles are given their photograph, with which they are extremely pleased, and they exit UL with their photograph and the Whooperdink

The Professor sits down and gazes rapturously at his photograph

You still have a magic snowflake left. You still have the chance to make your dreams come true.

Snowflake Maker I still have two left. I only need one for my wish. What about you? Don't you have a wish?

Crystal (*thoughtfully*) Ye-es, but (*looking at Seth*) I was hoping it would come true without the help of magic. (*Still looking at Seth, but speaking to the Snowflake Maker*) What about Seth?

Snowflake Maker Well?

Seth (*looking at Crystal*) It's true, I do have one great wish, but ...

Crystal Maybe ours is the same wish, Seth. (*She holds out her hand to Seth*)

Seth (*taking her hand*) Maybe it is.

Crystal and Seth gaze into each other's eyes

Snowflake Maker Well, that saves a magic snowflake.

Crystal But don't forget your wish—to leave here for a place in the sun.

Snowflake Maker You know, I'm not sure I want to leave here after all.

Crystal ⎫
Seth ⎭ (*together*) What?

Snowflake Maker We-ell ... things have picked up here lately, it's really been quite lively ... and all things considered, I think I'd miss it. And then, I have a duty, you know, to make all this snow; I mean, not everybody can be a snowflake maker. (*He pauses*) Now what I really would like is a little spell off ...

Seth Spell?

Snowflake Maker Yes, say a fortnight's holiday, once a year. Yes, that would do nicely.

Seth In that case, why don't you use a magic snowflake to release my mother from her spell, so that she could do your job while you're away?

Crystal What a good idea.

Seth It'll be her punishment for the way she's behaved.

Crystal And to stop her behaving like that in the future, can you wish away her witching powers and make her a good, simple mortal like everyone else?

Seth Er—Crystal.

Crystal Yes, Seth?

Seth Please—not simple!

Crystal Oh dear, of course not!

Snowflake Maker Right. Here we go.

The Snowflake Maker closes his eyes tight shut, concentrates, and throws the magic snowflake at Salmonella. She unfreezes, and from here on is a typically nice mum—named Marcia, though understandably, the rest are cautious at first

Seth Hallo, Mum.

Marcia Hallo, Seth. What's happened? Gosh my arms are stiff.

Seth Er—you've probably been standing in a draught.

Marcia My word, it's chilly. What are we doing here?

Seth Ah, Mum, let me introduce you. The Snowflake Maker.

Marcia (*going and shaking hands*) Very pleased to meet you.

Seth Professor Percival Potterton.
Marcia (*going and shaking hands*) How do you do.
Seth And—Crystal.
Marcia Crystal ...

The others wait with bated breath

What a nice name. And such a pretty face!
Seth Mum, Mr Snowflake Maker would like to take a holiday each year, just for two weeks. Would you mind standing in for him while he's away?
Marcia Well ... not so long as he gives me something warm to stand in.

They all laugh and the atmosphere relaxes

Professor Oh, it really is a pleasure to know you now, Marcia!
Marcia (*to the Snowflake Maker*) Will I be able to use that machine?
Snowflake Maker Yes of course, me dear. I'll show you.

The Snowflake Maker and Marcia go to the snowflake machine DR *to make snowflakes. He calls over the Professor, Seth and Crystal and they all have a try*

Right. How about you all coming back with me to my place? We can all have a nice hot chocolate to celebrate.
Seth Chocolate!
Snowflake Maker And you can all help me to decide where I should go for my holidays.
All What a good idea, splendid, *etc.*
Seth Just a minute. You still have one magic snowflake left. (*Going and picking it up from beside the deckchair*) Here.
Snowflake Maker The last magic snowflake. What shall I do with it? (*He pauses*) I know, I know! We'll use it for all the children here tonight. (*To the children*) Go on, make your own very special wish. And, if it's a good one, and you keep it a secret, may—it—come—true!

The Snowflake Maker throws the magic snowflake, in a sweeping motion, over the audience, who are showered by "magic snow"

Professor Well, that's absolutely splendid, absolutely fantastic! I've never seen anything like it; I must say——
Crystal Oh, Father!
Professor Yes. Er—I must say I'm ready for that chocolate. How about you, Marcia? (*He offers his arm*)
Marcia (*taking his arm*) I'd be delighted—Percival.

They start to move, arm in arm, followed by Seth and Crystal, arm in arm. The Snowflake Maker follows

Snowflake Maker I understand that Majorca is very pleasant this time of year ...

Everyone exits

The Lights fade to Black-out

THE RAILWAY CHILDREN
by E. Nesbit, adapted by Dave Simpson

In this adaptation of E. Nesbit's classic, set at the beginning of the twentieth century, Perks, the stationmaster, is the narrator of the play, linking the events, but also playing a leading role in some scenes. The family has settled at Three Chimneys Cottage after the disappearance of their father. Only Mother knows the cause at this point. Roberta, Peter and Phyllis become friendly with the Perks family and an old gentleman on the train, and then Mother becomes ill. There are several scene changes in this extract: from the station to the cottage and to the tunnel, and it is important to plan the staging carefully, with minimal time lapse as one scene moves to the next.

Set: A country railway station, a cottage, a railway tunnel. Period: Victorian/Edwardian.

Cast: M2 F1. 3 boys 3 girls.
Perks, the station porter. Roberta, Phyllis and Peter, the railway children. Mother. Doctor Forrest. Alfred, John and Edith, the Perks's children.

Playing time: 15 minutes.

Perks They used to come to the station every day, ten fifteen sharp. Each morning they'd stand on the platform 'ere and wave to the old gentleman.

Roberta, Peter and Phyllis wave as Perks speaks

Children Send our love to Father.
Perks And each day the old gentleman'd wave back to 'em as regular as clockwork.

The children exit

Perks moves the points and the set changes to the cottage

Their mam used to write you know. Short stories. And she tried to sell 'em. Now I'm all right at telling stories but not much use at writing 'em.

Mother is working at a laid table. The children join her and she sets aside her papers

Anyroad, she were that busy the three kids only seemed to see her at meal times. And for the first time in their lives they knew the meaning o' poverty.

Mother Phyllis, darling, jam or butter, not jam and butter.

Phyllis Oh, Mother.

Mother We can't afford that sort of luxury nowadays, darling.

Perks And when they hadn't enough food their mam'd say ...

Mother I'm not very hungry today, my lovelies, you eat the rest of this.

Perks But now and again their mam'd announce ...

Mother I've sold a story, my darlings.

Peter Oh smashing!

Phyllis That's terrific, Mother.

Perks And they'd all have buns for tea. They loved that. But most times they were like me; couldn't afford nothing fancy. Course, the way their mam neglected herself it weren't long afore she fell ill, poor thing ...

Mother leaves the table and mounts the stairs to her bed

She were so bad one morning she hadn't even the strength to get out o' bed.

Peter and Phyllis exit

Roberta moves up to join her

Roberta Oh Mother, how are you?

Mother I don't know what all the fuss is about. I only have a headache, that's all, and a little sore throat.

Roberta Your face is very red.

Mother That's because it's so warm in here.

Roberta touches her mother

Roberta Mother, it's freezing cold in here, but you're burning.

Mother I'm perfectly well. A day in bed and I'll be fine.

Roberta The doctor will be here in a minute.

Mother I don't know why you wanted to call the doctor in the first place. We shouldn't be bothering him, I'm sure he's busy enough as it is. And anyway we really can't afford a doctor.

Roberta Would you like a cup of tea, Mother?

Mother It's very kind of you, Bobby, but I don't want you fussing. I'm perfectly well enough to make my own tea. (*She tries to get out of bed but fails*)

Roberta Mother, are you all right?

Mother A little dizzy, that's all.

The Doctor enters downstairs with Peter and Phyllis, and goes up to Mother's room

Doctor Now then, what have we here? Good-morning. I'm Doctor Forrest.

Mother (*shaking hands*) Very pleased to meet you. I'm terribly sorry to bring you out.

Doctor Not at all. How are you?

Mother I don't want to be any trouble to you, Doctor.

Doctor And you won't be. (*To the children*) Anyway, I'd like you all to leave the room while I examine your mother. I won't be long.

The children leave the cottage to play in the garden

Perks Dr Forrest spent about ten minutes examining their mam and when he came out he wanted to speak to Roberta.

The Doctor enters the garden

Roberta How is she?

Doctor She's going to be fine.

Roberta She isn't *very* ill, is she?

Doctor Not at all. She has influenza.

Roberta Is that serious?

Doctor Not if we all look after her. Now, what's your name, young lady?

Roberta Roberta.

Doctor Well Roberta, I expect you'll want to be head nurse.

Roberta Oh yes.

Doctor Then I'll send down some medicine. Light up a fire in the room. Have some strong beef tea made ready to give her as soon as the fever goes down. She can have grapes now, and beef essence—and soda water and milk, and you'd better get a bottle of brandy. The best brandy. Cheap brandy is worse than poison. There are one or two other things and I've written them all down for you. (*He hands Roberta a list*)

Roberta Thank you. Only ...

Doctor Yes? (*A pause*) Only what? Out with it.

Roberta It's rather hard you see—to ... out with it. Because—because of what Mother said.

Doctor What *did* she say?

Roberta She said I wasn't to go telling everyone that we're poor. But you aren't everyone, are you?

Doctor Not at all. So?

Roberta Well ... I know doctors are very extravagant ... I mean expensive, and Mrs
Viney told me that her doctoring only cost her twopence a week because she
belonged to a club ...

Doctor Ah ...

Roberta You see she told me what a good doctor you were and I asked her how she
could afford you and then she told me about the club and I thought I'd ask you and
... oh Doctor, I don't want Mother to be worried. Can't we join the club too, the
same as Mrs Viney?

A pause. The Doctor smiles and sighs

You aren't cross with me are you?

Doctor Cross? How could I be? You're a very sensible lady. And you mustn't worry.
I'll make sure everything is fine with your mother even if I have to make a special
brand new club.

Roberta Oh thank you, Doctor.

Doctor So stop worrying. And that's doctor's orders. Now take that list up to your
mother and I'll come and visit her again very soon.

Roberta Thank you very, very much, Doctor.

The Doctor exits

Roberta goes into Mother's room

Mother, the doctor's given me this list.

Mother takes it, looks at it and gives a little laugh

Mother I can't afford all this rubbish, my lovely. Tell Mrs Viney to boil two pounds
of scrag end of neck for your dinner tomorrow and I can have some of the broth.
There's a shilling on the sideboard to buy it. I should like a glass of water now and
then I'll be perfectly happy. All right?

Roberta Yes, Mother.

Roberta leaves Mother's room and joins Phyllis and Peter in the garden

We've got to do something. Mother won't get well if we can't buy all the things on
this list.

Phyllis But we haven't got any money.

Roberta She's given me a shilling to buy some scrag end of neck for our tea but
she's just going to have the broth.

Peter We can do without the beastly mutton. Bread and butter will support life.
People have lived on less on desert islands many a time.

Phyllis But even if we don't have anything to eat at all we still won't have enough
money to get all those things.
Roberta No. We must think of some other way.
Perks And that's what they did. They thought harder than they'd ever thought before.
And after a long long time they came up with an idea.

Peter and Phyllis exit and then enter with a large white sheet

Roberta Now take that down to the tunnel, hold it up high so the old gentleman can
see, and I'll wait at the station. You understand that?
Phyllis Yes
Roberta Peter?
Peter Of course I understand.
Roberta Go on then. Hurry. We haven't much time.

Peter, Roberta and Phyllis exit

Perks And at ten fifteen Peter and Phyllis held high their white sheet with the message,
just as the train passed by.

Perks moves the points and the set changes to the tunnel

*Peter and Phyllis enter and stand at the front of the tunnel. On their sheet are
written the words "LOOK OUT AT THE STATION"*

The train passes. Perks moves the points and the set changes to the station

Peter and Phyllis exit

And Roberta rushed down to the station and got there as the train arrived.

Roberta enters the station, a note in her hand

A train pulls in behind the station double doors. Much steam, etc.

Roberta rushes on to the platform. Perks follows

Roberta (*off*) Sir ... sir ... please take this note and read it. Please sir, we need help.
Perks (*off*) Be careful, girl, that's dangerous.

John, Alfred and Edith enter. Perks brings Roberta in, back off the platform

(*To Roberta*) I don't know what you were doing, young girl, but you could've got
yourself killed.

Roberta I'm sorry, Mr Perks.

Perks Just you remember in future. (*He turns to leave, then pauses to speak to his children*) You're not up to no mischief, are you?

All No, Dad.

Perks That's all right.

Perks exits

John What were you doin' anyroad?

Roberta Oh hallo.

Alfred What were you givin' that old gentleman?

Roberta Just a note.

Edith What for?

Roberta To help Mother.

John How is she now?

Roberta She's still not well. You see the doctor's given us this list of things Mother needs but we just can't afford to buy them.

Edith What's that to do with the old gentleman?

Roberta We were—we were asking him for help.

John You mean scrounging?

Roberta Sorry. I don't understand.

John That's scrounging.

Roberta What d'you mean?

Alfred It's like begging.

Roberta It never is!

Edith I'd scrounge if my mam were ill.

Roberta Of course you would—and anyway—it isn't ... scrounging as you call it.

John I call it scrounging.

Roberta You would.

John You don't even know him.

Roberta Yes we do!

John Have you ever spoken to him?

Roberta Not exactly—but we've waved.

Alfred What's his name?

Roberta The old gentleman.

John Is that his first name or his second?

John and Alfred laugh

Roberta Anyway, I don't care what you think—I'd do anything to make sure Mother gets well again—so there. (*And she turns on her heels and moves off*)

John (*after her*) We didn't mean it.

Roberta turns. John goes up to her so that they are on their own

We didn't. It's just—it's just that ... well ... you're a bit stuck up sometimes, aren't you?

Roberta I beg your pardon?

John You're a snob.

Roberta Oh no I'm not!

John Yes, y'are. You think you're too good for us, don't you?

Roberta No, I don't.

John You do.

Roberta Honestly I don't, I don't really.

John You're not like us though, are you?

Roberta I've never thought about it.

John Well you're not. Is your mam going to be all right?

Roberta Yes—if we can get all these things she needs.

John Can we help?

Roberta I don't think so—but thank you. (*She is about to go, but turns*) John— would you say you're poor?

John We're not rich.

Roberta But are you poor?

John No. Course we're not. Me dad'd go spare if he heard you say that.

Roberta Why?

John He just would.

Roberta Have you got a big house?

John It's the station house. It's big enough. Three bedrooms.

Roberta Three? For eight of you?

John That's big enough. Mam and Dad have their room with the baby. Edith, Emma and Joan share a bed in theirs, and me and me brothers have a bed in ours.

Roberta You all sleep together?

John Yeh. What's wrong wi' that?

Roberta It can't be very comfortable.

John It's OK—so long as you all turn over at the same time.

They all laugh

Anyroad ... best be going. Tara then.

Roberta Yes ... (*She hesitates but smiles*) Tara.

All the children exit

A train is heard

Perks enters and changes the points

The set changes to the cottage

Perks (*collecting a hamper*) That evening a big great hamper was delivered to the station, with a note to take it to the children at Three Chimneys Cottage. And that's what I did. (*He moves towards the cottage*)

Roberta, Peter and Phyllis are downstairs

Peter It's Mr Perks! With a large hamper!
Roberta It must be from the old gentleman.
Perks (*struggling breathlessly*) Oh my God! The hills don't get no smaller. This here's from the old gentleman. (*He drops the hamper on his foot and cries out*)
Roberta Thank you very much, Mr Perks. This is wonderful.
Perks I don't know about wonderful. It were blinking heavy!
Peter Thank you anyway.
Perks S'all right. Anyroad ... hmm ... (*Blowing*) I'm out o' puff ... now ... Hmm.
Peter (*quickly*) Oh I'm awfully sorry, I haven't got twopence to give you like Father does, but ...
Perks I beg your pardon, young lad?
Peter Well Father always tips twopence to——
Perks I don't want none o' your twopence. I were just about to ask how your mother is, that's all.
Peter Oh, I'm awfully sorry.
Perks And I've fetched her along a bit o' sweetbriar, that's what I were going to say.
Roberta Oh we're terribly sorry, I hope Peter didn't offend you.
Perks Anyroad, here y'are. (*And he produces a bunch of sweetbriar from his hat*)
Roberta It's very kind of you.
Perks That's all right.
Peter And I really do beg your pardon about the twopence, Mr Perks.
Perks We'll just forget it, eh?
Peter Yes.
Perks And I'll wish you a good-night and hope your mother's better soon.

The children bid him good-night

Perks exits

Peter Come on then, let's get it open.

Excitedly the children open the hamper

Roberta Oh there's more here than we asked for.
Phyllis Peaches!
Roberta Port wine!
Peter I'll have some of that.

Roberta No you certainly won't!
Phyllis A chicken!
Roberta Oh and look at these roses.
Phyllis What a kind gentleman he is.
Peter Here's a letter!
Roberta Oh. Read it out.
Peter (*reading*) "Dear Roberta, Phyllis and Peter. Here are the things you want. Your mother will want to know where they came from. Tell her they were sent by a friend who heard she was ill. When she is well again you must tell her all about it, of course. And if she says you ought not to have asked for the things, tell her that I say you were quite right, and that I hope she will forgive me for taking the liberty of allowing myself a great pleasure." It's signed GP. I can't read that properly.
Phyllis Well I think we were right.
Roberta Right? Of course we were right.
Peter All the same I don't exactly look forward to telling Mother the whole truth about it.
Roberta We're not to do it till she's well and when she's well we'll be so happy we shan't mind a little fuss like that. Now—take the roses up to her.
Phyllis And the sweetbriar!
Roberta Oh yes, you mustn't forget the sweetbriar!

Peter and Phyllis exit with the flowers. Perks enters and moves the points

The set changes to the tunnel

Perks And within two weeks their mam was much better. So they got out another banner and when the ten fifteen came out of the tunnel Phyllis and Peter were there to greet it.

Peter and Phyllis enter and stand before the tunnel. They have a sheet with the words: "SHE IS NEARLY WELL THANK YOU"

ROBIN HOOD
by David Wood and Dave and Toni Arthur

A group of villagers act one of the playlets from the Robin Hood legend, set at a May Day celebration. The story is told in rhyme, with music, dancing and singing. There is much opportunity for invention in presenting this amusing tale.

Set: An open space, such as a village green, where the May Games took place. Period: legendary.

Cast: M8 F4, 1M or F. Extras.
All are villagers acting in the play: Philip, the 'Butcher'. Peter, the Jack-in-the-Green, 'Robin Hood'. Bendick, 'Little John'. Alan, 'Sheriff of Nottingham'. Tessa, a serving girl at the beer bower, 'Sheriff of Nottingham's wife'. Elizabeth, the ale wife, an older, buxom hostess. Jan, a milkmaid, dressed all in white. Dorcas, a milkmaid at the beer bower. George, a morris dancer. Pedlars, two men. John, a 'trader'. Narrator. Villagers to play a 'Servant', 'Attendants' and 'Deer'.

Playing time: 12 minutes.

Tessa ⎱	Wild flowers!
Elizabeth ⎰	Wild flowers!
(*or children*)	
Jan ⎱	Fresh milk and warm,
Dorcas ⎰	Straight from the cow!
Pedlars (*2 men*)	I've got ribbons and pins
	And bright shiny buttons,
	And sugar and gingerbread!
Three Men	We have got good ale, boys
	Oh we have got good ale!
Butcher	I've got beef and venison!

The villager who is the butcher subsequently becomes the "Butcher"

All   May games, May games,
                   Ev'rything for your May games!
                   May games, May games,
                   Ev'rything for your May Games!

This leads to a complicated counterpoint section, in which all the cries are sung on top of one another. Finally ...

Butcher   I've got beef and venison!

He realizes he is singing on his own, and looks embarrassed. The others wander off leaving him alone, c

                   I've got beef and venison!

He is rescued by George, who comes forward playing his lute/guitar

The Lights change to focus on George, and the Butcher

Everyone else becomes an audience, until required in the story

George   We'll tell you a tale of this butcher so bold
                   On his way to the market one morning
                   As he walked through the wood
                   In a flash, Robin Hood
                   Jumped on him without any warning.

"Robin Hood" appears from the shadows and grabs the "Butcher", who takes out his knife, threateningly. They grapple, but eventually "Robin Hood" proves himself the stronger, disarms the "Butcher" and pinions him from behind, an arm round his neck

"Robin Hood"   Not so fast master butcher, if you value your life,
                   I'm not one of your herd to be stuck with a knife.
                   Where are you going?
"Butcher"   To Market in Nottingham.
"Robin Hood"   Open your bags and let's see what you've got in 'em.

A Narrator takes up the tale

Narrator   When he saw all the meat, Robin had an idea.
                   He said,

"Robin Hood"   Master butcher, you've nothing to fear;
                          Your meat and your cart, your apron and hat—
                          I'll pay a fair price if you sell me all that.

Narrator   The price was agreed and a bargain was struck;
                          The butcher could hardly believe his good luck.

   The "Butcher" departs happily

                          And Robin's eyes twinkled as they said their goodbyes,
"Robin Hood" (*to the audience*) The Sheriff is going to get a surprise.

                          For it's said that he's put a price on my head,
                          But I fancy that he'll pay the price instead.
Narrator   So he trundled the cart to Nottingham Market,
                          And found by the castle a good place to park it.

*"Robin Hood" mimes his journey. Another "Trader" sets up his stall nearby.
"Shoppers" suggest a market*

                          He wasn't the only meat butcher around
"Trader"   Come buy my fresh venison, fivepence a pound.

The "Shoppers" crowd round him. "Robin Hood" sets up his stall

"Robin Hood"   He's cheating you rotten, fair ladies and gents.
                   Come buy *my* fresh venison, a pound for *four* pence.

The "Shoppers" transfer their custom to "Robin Hood"

"Trader"   Now don't wander off, folks, just listen to me,
                   Today's special offer, five pence down to three.

The "Shoppers" ooh and aah with pleasure and return to the "Trader"

"Robin Hood"   Wait! My cut price cuts are cheaper than any,
                   Come buy my fresh venison, a pound for one penny.

The "Shoppers" return to "Robin Hood". The "Trader" shrugs and departs

                   Those fly-by-night traders, you never can trust 'em.
                   Two pounds for you, madam? Thanks for your custom.

Narrator	News of the bargain spread fast through the town.
	From the castle, the wife of the Sheriff came down.

Fanfare as the "Sheriff's Wife" greedily enters and barges her way through the "Shoppers"

"Sheriff's Wife"	Butcher, this venison, how much have you got?
"Robin Hood"	I've thirteen pounds left, lady.
"Sheriff's Wife"	I'll take the lot.
	But it looks such a weight.
Narrator	Smiled Robin,
"Robin Hood"	No trouble;
	Delivery's free, I'll be up at the double.

Pleased, the "Sheriff's Wife" leads "Robin Hood" to an area representing the castle

Narrator	Robin's plan was succeeding; he carried the parcel
	All the way up to and into the castle.

After miming his journey, "Robin Hood" hands the meat to the "Sheriff's Wife"

"Sheriff's Wife"	*(aside)* This butcher, if pampered, I firmly conclude will
	Be fearfully good for the size of my food bill.
	(To "Robin Hood") Good Butcher, don't go, have a goblet of wine?
	And do us the honour of staying to dine.
Narrator	Said Robin Hood,
"Robin Hood"	Thanks!
Narrator	And thus found himself able
	To sit with his enemy, the Sheriff, at table.

The "Sheriff" enters

"Sheriff"	Come in!
Narrator	Leered the Sheriff.
"Sheriff"	Pray do take your place.
"Robin Hood"	I'll take,
Narrator	thought bold Robin
"Robin Hood"	that smile off your face!

They sit at a table to dine. A "Servant" brings wine and food

Narrator	With flattering words his praises he sung,
	Till the wine started loos'ning the Sheriff's tongue.

He told tales of corruption, of cheating and guile,
Of men he'd imprisoned without any trial.

Of rigging and fixing, of bribing the jury;
Robin heartily laughed, thus disguising his fury.

"Sheriff"   What a splendid repast, your meat was delicious.
But where did it come from?
Narrator   He was getting suspicious.
"Sheriff"   Did you filch it?
Narrator   Cried Robin,
"Robin Hood"   No, don't be absurd.
For years I've been breeding my own special herd.
My beasts are the finest from Lincoln to York.
"Sheriff"   You're lying, good butcher, you're all wind and talk.
"Robin Hood"   Come and see for yourself, that I don't overrate them.

"Sheriff"   I *will* come and see them, (*aside*) and then confiscate them!

He beckons two "Attendants" to follow him

Narrator   So after their meal without any delay
Deep into the forest they wended their way.

*Music. "Robin Hood", "Sheriff", plus two "Attendants" set off. Others act trees or
obstacles to suggest the forest. The lighting turns sinister*

Through thicket and bramble, through stream and through ditch,
The Sheriff grew weary and started to twitch.
"Sheriff"   This isn't a trick?
"Robin Hood"   Sir, I give you my word,
Another few miles and you'll gaze on my herd.

"Robin Hood" suddenly blows his horn

You can trust me, sir,
Narrator   But the Sheriff cried,
"Sheriff"   But here in the forest the outlaws hide!

*During the next two verses, unseen by the "Sheriff", his two "Attendants" are
grabbed and carried off by "Robin Hood's men"*

They're vicious and ruthless, they're up to no good;
And the worst of them all calls himself Robin Hood.

He's escaped me so far, like a wriggly worm,
But if I ever set eyes on him, I'll make him squirm.

"Robin Hood"   Pray calm yourself, sir, you'll frighten the deer,
Look in that clearing and soon they'll appear.

Music as the "Deer" (villagers with antlers on their heads) enter and move around behind the trees or bushes, with only their antlers visible. (In the first London production, stools used in the Sheriff scene were picked up by the girls, who held them upside down over their heads to suggest antlers.) An eerie atmosphere

I kept my word, sir. Admit they're fine.
"Sheriff"   They are, good butcher, what is more they are *mine.*

The "Sheriff" pulls a knife on "Robin Hood". Drums for tension. "Robin Hood" pretends to be afraid

"Robin Hood"   I don't understand, sir.
"Sheriff"   Now don't be alarmed.
Just do as you're told and I'll see you're not harmed.

"Robin Hood"   How kind! But, sir, I don't need your protection;
For me these deer have a special affection.

They're faithful and loyal and honest and true
You may fancy them, but they don't fancy you!

Percussion noises begin as the antlered villagers reveal themselves as "Outlaws", and start approaching the "Sheriff" menacingly

Take them out of the wood, if you reckon you could,
But first you must reckon with—Robin Hood!

Music, as "Robin Hood" reveals himself. The "Sheriff", in his confusion, finds his knife wrenched from his hand

"Sheriff"   Y-y-you're Robin Hood? Get him!
(*Looking round, then realizing his "Men" are gone*)
                              Where are my men?
"Robin Hood"   In heaven—or hell! You'll not see them again.
Come on, sir, I'm waiting—I'm your wriggly worm.
Now you've set eyes on me, pray make me squirm.

"Robin Hood" advances. The "Sheriff" retreats

"Sheriff"   You'll pay for this, Hood, you'll hang by your toes!
"Robin Hood" Oh no, sir, *you'll* pay, you'll pay through the nose.

Music, as the antlered villagers approach and surround the "Sheriff"

"Sheriff"   Mercy, I beg you, sir, please spare my life,
                  For the sake of my children, for the sake of my wife.

"Robin Hood" But what of the price you put on my head?
                  (*To the others*) Should I let him live, when he wished me dead?

The others shake their heads or cry "no"

"Sheriff"   I swear by our Lady, if you set me free
                  Your safety in Sherwood, will I guarantee.

Pause

"Robin Hood" Very well, sir, I b'lieve you, but b'lieve me you'll find
                  That if there's a next time we won't be so kind.

George comes forward

George   The Sheriff had made them a promise
                  So the outlaws escorted him back
                  And so he couldn't retrace
                  His steps to this place
                  They covered his head with a sack.

As the girls cover the "Sheriff's" head with a sack, the "Outlaws" take his money and valuables

SECOND FROM LAST IN THE SACK RACE
by Michael Birch from the novel by David Nobbs

Set in the North of England, this clever and fast-moving play is about Henry Pratt from his birth in 1935 until 1953. When his father 'joins up' at the start of the war in 1939, Henry and his mother, Ada, stay with relatives. These scenes tell of Henry's change of lifestyle in facing new people in and out of school, especially when his mother is run over by a bus.

Set: A barn, on a train, in the Headmistress' study, a classroom and playground.
The four scenes are set as simply as possible, and move from one to the next by positioning and use of the acting space. Period: 1940-45.

Cast: M7 F3, may be played by M5 F2.
Henry Pratt, aged about 8 years plus. Eric Lugg, a teenager from a family of trouble-makers, 'Henry's foe with a hoe'. Lorna Arrow, the same age as Henry, flighty and excitable, 'Henry's forward first girlfriend'. Miss Candy, 'Henry's dedicated first teacher'. Miss Forest, 'Henry's desiccated headmistress'. Mr Gibbins, 'Henry's weary second teacher', sincere, but weary of boys in general. Martin Hammond, Tommy Marsden, Basher and Slasher: Paradise Lane Gang members.

Playing time: 13 minutes.

SCENE A

Comic cut-outs. Henry reads the "Beano" in a barn

Eric Lugg enters, an almost grown-up lad from a family of trouble-makers. Eric carries a venomous-looking hoe

Eric What's tha doing in this barn?
Henry Oh cripes! It's Eric Lugg! Look at that hoe!
Eric Ay, lad, mark it well. Eric Lugg I be. And tha's trespassing, squirt.
Henry This barn belongs to Lorna Arrow's dad. She said I could be here. I'm waiting for her.

Eric Hang on, I know thee. You're that cissy squirt evacuee from up at Turnbulls.

Henry I'm not an evacuee. I'm staying wi' relations. I'm not afraid of thee, tha don't own this barn, you Luggs don't own anything, apart from a rat-infested cottage and a back garden full of rusty bikes and sundry bric-à-brac.

Eric I'm a terror round these parts, does tha know that, pansy?

Henry Me Uncle Frank and me Aunty Kate say that you Luggs should be put a stop to. They reckon you're a blemish on the face of Rowth Bridge village.

Eric I'll kill thee!

Henry No tha won't.

Eric I'll skewer thee wi' me hoe!

Henry Tha wouldn't dare.

Eric I'll stand next to thee and give thee nits.

Henry Don't tha come near me.

Eric Tha's teacher's pet, in't tha?

Henry Miss Candy is interested in my progress, that's all. She doesn't believe in favouritism.

Eric Has tha seen her titties?

Henry (*squealing with shock*) Eeooaagh!

Eric We all know she has a moustache, 'cos we can see it, and that she's as fat as a pregnant cow, but does tha know she's got great tufts of hair all over?

Henry Tha's making it up. How does tha know?

Eric She used to be stripper in a club.

Henry Where?

Eric Wakefield.

Henry I don't believe it.

Eric And she keeps a giant seal in her bath.

Henry What for?

Eric She used to train 'em in t'circus. And she swigs a bottle of gin a day. And she was loved by a Yank who ran off and left her. Who'd blame him? But does tha know what she does to her favourite cissy teacher's pet after about a month or two?

Henry What, Eric, what does she do?

Eric Er ... Tha'll find out. Now clear out.

Lorna Arrow enters, a girl the same age as Henry, flighty and excitable, already a natural flirt

Lorna Oh, it's horrid, smelly Eric Lugg. What on earth are you doing in my dad's barn?

Eric Just inspecting it, Miss Arrow.

Henry Hallo, Lorna.

Lorna (*to Eric*) Does tha take me for an infant? I am eight. You are backsliding and trying to get out of work. What was he saying to you, Henry?

Henry He was just saying funny things about Miss Candy.

Lorna Oh you disgusting beast! Spreading those vile rumours. I wouldn't be surprised if only half of them are totally true. Miss Candy is just a poor, maligned spinster school-teacher of fifty-three who's hideously ugly. Was he frightening you, Henry? I bet he was.

Henry (*doubtfully*) No.

Eric Cissy'd be frightened of a runt piglet.

Lorna Leave this barn on the instant, or I shall report you to my dad, and then that will be the end of casual employment on the Arrows' farm for you!

Eric All right, I'm going. (*Threatening them*) But I'm not running away. Some of us have got to bale hay. (*To Henry*) Eh, lad, keep thy hand on tha sixpence, she'll violate thy purity given half a chance. Ha, ha, ha.

Eric Lugg exits, laughing

Lorna Hallo. Which does tha prefer, Henry, greengages or eggs?

Henry Both.

Lorna Tha can have a greengage for tha breakfast then. Ha, ha. (*Then, suggestively*) Come and sit down next to me and read comics to me.

Henry Me mood isn't right. Does tha think I'm advanced for me years?

Lorna (*suggestively again*) Ay, I do. I think tha's right good at tha lessons too. No, really!

Henry (*mystified by her strange tone*) That's all right, I know I am.

Lorna Conceitedness is not at all a nice thing in a boy. Any road ... (*she chants*) ... you're a fat useless lump, that's what everybody says.

Henry I aren't. I'll show you.

Lorna Oh do, do, do!

Henry Don't want to.

Lorna Who was the only person not to laugh at you on sports day?

Henry I didn't come last in everything.

Lorna No, not in the sack race, but I think you are forgetting the hundred yards, the four forty, the egg and spoon race, the high jump, the three-legged race and potato race. Last every time is quite a record.

Pause. Lorna suddenly lifts her skirt, showing him her knickers briefly. Henry blinks in confusion and disbelief

Any road, it's the holidays now. Yippee!

Lorna chases Henry. He tries to avoid her and do something safer, like reading his comic

Henry I'll read to thee. Lord Snooty and his pals ...

Lorna I'm bored with that. Which would tha prefer, Henry, a castle with six gold doors or sixteen tons of All Bran?

Henry Which would tha prefer, a smack in the gob or a kick up t'arse end?

Lorna exits screaming tearfully

SCENE B

Sounds of a third division football match followed by that of a train journey

Miss Candy is escorting young Henry. Miss Candy has a far-back voice

Miss Candy Well, Henry, and what did you think of the game?
Henry It were the greatest football match in the world, miss.
Miss Candy Wasn't it just, Henry?! And are you enjoying the train ride?
Henry Oh, ay, miss.
Miss Candy There's no better team on God's earth than Bradford City, even in the Wartime League North.
Henry In the first half I supported Leeds and they scored two goals, and second half I supported Bradford and they scored two goals, so I was supporting winning side throughout t'match. That was good, wasn't it, miss?
Miss Candy That was very good, Henry.
Henry (*in wonderment*) Are they really greatest team on God's earth, are they, miss?
Miss Candy No, I'm sorry, Henry, not really, but it's great fun to think so. Getting all excited and worked up! Shouting at the ref, "Other way, ref! Where's your white stick, you fool!" It's so exhilarating.
Henry Miss Candy?
Miss Candy Yes, Henry.
Henry Me dad's coming home on leave soon. He's been wounded. In his eye. Me mam's going to Portsmouth to meet him. Miss Candy?
Miss Candy Yes, Henry.
Henry I want to stay at your school. I don't ever want to leave Low Farm, ever.
Miss Candy You'll have to go back to your own home when the war's over.
Henry You know, I were right bothered at match when tha were shouting and everything. All the men were looking at you.
Miss Candy Yes, but they tend to do that anyway.
Henry I don't think tha needs a shave, Miss Candy.

A slight pause

Miss Candy That's very kind of you. Henry, since you have had such an enjoyable day, I want you to do something for me. I know people say certain things about me. I want you to tell me what they say, Henry. It'll be good for me.
Henry Everything?

Miss Candy Oh yes, absolutely everything.

Pause

Henry Oh double heck.

SCENE C

The Lights come up on Miss Forest, headmistress, in her room. Miss Forest is a brisk, no-nonsense, self-confident and self-righteous headmistress

Miss Candy enters in high dudgeon

Miss Candy Miss Forest.
Miss Forest Miss Candy.
Miss Candy Just now ...
Miss Forest Yes.
Miss Candy Miss Forest, just now without so much as a by-your-leave the Pratt boy was whisked out of my classroom ...
Miss Forest By me.
Miss Candy By you. And if I may say so in a most imperious manner.
Miss Forest I am sorry that you feel belittled by my actions, Miss Candy ...
Miss Candy I didn't say that.
Miss Forest May I be clear what is required?
Miss Candy I wish you to knock on my classroom door before entering in future.
Miss Forest You do?
Miss Candy I do.
Miss Forest At all times, Miss Candy?
Miss Candy It seems reasonable, Miss Forest.
Miss Forest I take it you wouldn't object if I were to omit the knock in the case of a fire for example?
Miss Candy Obviously not in the case of a fire.
Miss Forest Or in the case of an act of God, Miss Candy?
Miss Candy In the case of an act of God, yes, you may omit the knock, Miss Forest.
Miss Forest Thank you. How about in the case of the Pratt boy's mother being run over by a bus?

A slight pause

Miss Candy Has the Pratt boy's mother been run over by a bus?
Miss Forest (*smiling at Miss Candy*) Yes, Miss Candy, isn't it terrible? The driver stood no chance. It happened in Portsmouth. Ada Pratt had apparently gone there

to greet her husband. She was crossing the road, about to embrace him, I believe. Tragic, under the circumstances, I'm sure you'll agree, Miss Candy?

Miss Candy I'm sorry, I ...

Miss Forest I accept your apology.

Pause

Miss Candy Miss Forest ...?

Miss Forest Naturally the boy will be returning to live with his father in Thurmarsh. Now if you will excuse me ...

Miss Candy Poor Henry.

Miss Forest We can't afford to be sentimental, can we? After all there is a war on, or rather, there was. A word about your teaching methods, I don't approve of favouritism, and neither do the parents. I thought I'd mention it. Good. Now, the VE Day celebrations. I trust I can leave the catering to you?

Radio comedy programmes are heard

SCENE D

The Lights come up on Mr Gibbins's classroom

Mr Gibbins is a sincere but weary teacher, weary of boys in general and these boys in particular

Henry enters

Henry Er ... is this Form Two?

Mr Gibbins You must be the new boy. The returning evacuee.

Henry I weren't an evacuee. I were staying with relations.

Mr Gibbins Same thing.

Henry I were staying at Low Farm. It's at Rowth Bridge, Upper Mitherdale.

Mr Gibbins Oh, a geography specialist.

The boys laugh, Henry is mortified

Well, welcome back to Thurmarsh, near Sheffield. I'm Mr Gibbins. Who are you?

Henry Henry.

Mr Gibbins Henry what?

Henry Henry Pratt.

Mr Gibbins Henry Pratt what?

Henry Just Henry Pratt.

Mr Gibbins At your last school, in Rowth Bridge, Upper Mitherdale——

Sniggers from the boys

—if your teacher had said, "What is your name?" what would you have said?
Henry Ezra.
Mr Gibbins I thought you said your name was Henry.
Henry Ay, it is, but there were another Henry, and they couldn't have two Henrys so they called me Ezra in t'school.
Mr Gibbins I see. Now Pratt, when you addressed your teacher, in Rowth Bridge, Upper Mitherdale——

More sniggers

—did you use a little word as a mark of respect to that teacher?
Henry Oh ay.
Mr Gibbins Well, we believe in respect for authority here at Brunswick Road Primary, so I'd like you to use the same little word to me. Do you understand?
Henry Oh ay.
Mr Gibbins Oh ay what?
Henry Oh ay, miss.

Mr Gibbins is non-plussed. The boys collapse in laughter. Change of scene. Playground noise

The Paradise Lane Gang enter

Hallo, Martin, hallo, Tommy, hallo, Basher, hallo, Slasher.
Gang Hallo, Henry.
Henry What's Paradise Lane Gang doing tonight?

The boys tap their noses and jeer

Martin We all know what you're doing! You're looking after your one-eyed dad.

Laughter

Henry Me dad lost that eye fighting Germans, Martin Hammond!
Basher I heard he'd pawned it down t'*Navigation* pub for half a pint.

Laughter

Martin (*pointing to his eye*) Ay, ay.

Laughter

Henry I'll get thee, Martin Hammond!

Henry tries to hit Martin. The boys beat Henry to the ground.

Gang Bye, Henry.

STONE SOUP
by Paul Thain

This play is a modern fable, but based on an ancient folk tale. An old woman, Sophia, comes to a starving village and sets about convincing the people that the only way to survive is to share what little food they have. There is a special style and ritual about the stirring and sounds of the soup, and Sophia has a magical quality of 'long ago' about her. Henry North, an Englishman, and his American wife, Martha, are superior characters, who have loaned their large cooking pot for the soup-making. The cast is flexible: an assortment of people from many nations.

Set: The Village: an open space, representing the square. It is littered with stones, and in the centre of the area is an enormous cooking pot with ladle.

Cast: M5 F5. Extras.
Sophia, a stranger to the village; old. Makomo. Camilla. Jason, her son. Doreen. Kausa. Thin Girl. Ti-Sung. Henry North, an Englishman; 50s. Martha North, his American wife; 40s. Villagers.

Playing time: 14 minutes.

Villagers Bloop, bloop, bloop ... Bloop, bloop, bloop, bloop ... Bloop, bloop, bloop ...
Makomo You know, perhaps Ahmed was not so crazy. I myself can smell this stone soup. And, do you know, it smells rather good.
Sophia Oh, you think so, do you? Well, what do you know, eh? Ha! I tell you this is nothing, nothing! I remember once I made stone soup with a little salt beef. Ah! Now that—that was magnificent! Truly magnificent!
Jason My mum's got some sa——

Camilla slaps Jason

Ow! What was that for?

Everyone looks at Camilla

Camilla Why are you all staring? Don't look at me like—well, all right, what if I
   have? It's only a tiny little——
Jason No, it's——

Camilla slaps him again

   Ow!

Sophia tuts. All eyes remain fixed on Camilla

Doreen You've got salt beef?
Camilla Doreen, it's miniscule. Microscopic. Tiny. Hardly worth the——
Doreen You had my bleedin' cabbage quick enough!
Camilla Honest, love, it wouldn't——
Doreen Honest? Honest! I'm surprised you don't choke! You told me you had
   nothing'! You rotten, two-faced——
Camilla Here! Who are you calling——
Doreen I'll tell you who I'm calling——
Camilla Oh, you will, will you?
Doreen Yes, I will.
Camilla Oh yeah?
Doreen Yeah!

Camilla and Doreen begin to wrestle

Sophia Ladies, please, please!
Camilla I'll kill her, I will—I will, I'll—ow!
Doreen Serves you right!
Sophia Oh, dear, dear, dear——(*She raises her staff*)

*The Lights flash and a crash of thunder is heard. Doreen and Camilla immediately
stop fighting and look up at the sky, astonished*

   Have you heard nothing? We should not fight, we must help one another!

There is a pause. Doreen and Camilla look chastened

Doreen (*to Camilla*) Well? You heard. So what's it to be?
Camilla Oh, all right then. (*She moves to exit*) Only God knows what my Fred'll
   say.

   Camilla exits to fetch the salt beef during the following

Doreen (*calling off*) Oh, and bring some garlic. I like garlic. An' don't say you've
  got none 'cos I know you have!
Villagers Bloop, bloop, bloop, ... Bloop, bloop, bloop, bloop ... Bloop, bloop, bloop ...

Sophia stirs the soup. The Thin Girl approaches the pot

Sophia You again.
Thin Girl Please, is it ready yet?
Sophia No, my child, I'm sorry, but you must be patient.

The girl turns away sadly

Villagers Bloop, bloop, bloop, ... Bloop, bloop, bloop, bloop ... Bloop, bloop, bloop ...

Ti-Sung helps to stir the contents of the pot

  Bloop, bloop, bloop, ... Bloop, bloop, bloop, bloop ... Bloop, bloop, bloop ...
Ti-Sung My father was a brave man; I think you would have liked him. Many times
  he risked his life calling for justice. Even when they put him in prison, he wouldn't
  stay silent. The last time I saw him, not long before they killed him, he told me—
  he told me if I dream of a better world I help to make it real. Do you believe that?
  Do you think it can be true?
Sophia Of course it's true. We are in the world and the world is in us. The world, it
  is made of dreams, many, many dreams, each a possible future, each future struggling
  to shape reality. If we let them, the bad dreams, the greedy dreams will eat us all
  up. But the good ones—the good dreams, they are hungry for change, and if we
  are wise they will nourish our world with peace and plenty.
Ti-Sung But how can we tell the good dreams from the bad?
Sophia Ah, it is not so difficult. That which brings us together is good. That which
  divides us is bad. What could be more simple? Now listen, come closer, listen to
  the pot. Well? Do you hear? Can you hear?

*The Villagers "bloop" to the tune of Bach's "Jesu, Joy of Man's Desiring", Sophia
conducting with her staff. Ti-Sung nods and smiles. As this interlude ends, the Thin
Girl approaches the pot again*

Thin Girl Please, is it ready yet?
Sophia Haven't I told you? Why can't you wait like the rest?

The Girl turns sadly away

  I'm sorry, my child, but you must be patient.

Henry and Martha enter in a comic car, tooting the horn loudly; the car backfires and gives off lots of smoke

Henry Well, hallo there.
Martha Hi.
Sophia Mr and Mrs North.

Henry and Martha eagerly make for the pot. Martha stares into the pot and sniffs

Henry (*to Sophia and the Villagers*) No, no, please, no need for ceremony—just happened to be passing.
Martha Mmmm—smells wonderful!
Henry (*to Martha*) Weren't we, darling? Darling?
Martha Hmm? Oh. Yes, that's right—just passing. You know, just passing by——
Henry Thought we'd drop in——
Martha See how all you good people are getting on.
Sophia You are most welcome!

Sophia, Martha and Henry stand awkwardly, exchanging smiles

Henry To be perfectly honest, we couldn't resist the soup, could we, darling?
Martha I don't suppose you do hamburgers.
Sophia Hamburgers? What? Cow in a bun? No, no, no, cows in buns, they cost the earth; I make soup, stone soup.
Henry What soup?
Sophia Stone soup.
Henry You mean soup made with—with——?
Sophia Stones; nice, fresh, juicy stones.
Martha Stones?
Sophia These are, of course, special stones.
Henry Ah, yes, I see.
Martha Well, I'm damned if I do.
Sophia It is an ancient peasant recipe.
Henry Amazing. Now isn't that amazing, darling, absolutely amazing? Stone soup, eh? Splendid! Now if that's not being resourceful, I don't know what is. Nothing like adversity to bring out the old native genius, eh?
Martha Soup made with stones? But—but how? It smells so good.
Henry Yes, well ... These peasant people, you see, darling, sons of the soil. Certainly know their onions when they get in a pickle, ha-ha. I remember once in Tuscany——
Martha Henry, please, you're giving me a migraine. Oh, excuse me, I feel quite—quite faint.
Sophia Oh, my poor dear!

Martha Don't you worry about me, I'll—I'll be all right.
Henry Darling, are you sure?
Martha It's probably just, you know—hunger.
Henry But darling—you've only just had lunch.
Martha Henry?
Henry Yes, darling?
Martha Shut up.
Henry Yes, darling. Sorry, darling.
Martha (*wobbling*) Oh, no, no, don't worry, I'll—I'll be fine. Probably.
Sophia Well, my soup, it is not quite ready yet, but would you like a little taste?
Martha Does a duck like water? (*She quickly recovers, seizes the ladle and takes a big, noisy slurp*) Oh, my dear ... (*She slurps again*) My dear, it's wonderful!

The Villagers nod and murmur appreciatively. Martha has another slurp

Henry Darling, do you ... do you think I might, might possibly ...?
Martha (*taking another slurp of the soup*) My God ... Oh, my God ... (*She slurps again*)
Henry Darling ...?
Martha Be quiet, Henry. (*She takes another slurp*) Mmm—this is so good. (*And another*)
Sophia Perhaps Mr North might also like to taste——?
Martha Excuse me? Oh, I'm sorry! Oh, my manners—what must you think! (*She hands the ladle to Henry*) Here, Henry, now don't you dare be greedy!
Henry Thank you, darling. (*He slurps the soup*) Oh, I say, now that is good.
Sophia Ah—you are too kind. But here ... let me try ... (*She takes the ladle and slurps the soup*) Ah, no, no, no, no ... it is still not right.
Martha You mean—you mean it could be even better——?
Sophia Well, as we know, only God is perfect. But I tell you something, just between ourselves: stone soup, stone soup with chicken, ah, now that—that is almost sacrilege!
Martha That means it's good, right?
Sophia Good? I tell you it is ambrosia!
Henry It does sound rather special. So, all we—all we need is a chicken, eh? Do we, er—do we happen to know anyone who might possibly have a chicken, dearest?
Martha Henry, I think we've contributed quite enough already!
Henry Ah, yes: the pot. Yes, indeed. It is our pot, you see. On hire.
Martha And on the most generous of terms. Not that we ever get any thanks. Oh, no. Why is it always us, eh? Why can't someone else bring a goddam chicken?
Sophia These people are poor, only you have chicken.
Martha Is that so? Well, that's just too bad.
Henry Oh. Oh dear.
Sophia Dear, oh dear ...

Henry What a pity.

Sophia Yes, a pity, a great pity, a great, great pity, a great, great, great pity—what a pity, such a pity.

Henry Stone soup with chicken, eh? Must be quite something ...

Sophia Oh, yes. Yes, indeed. Indeed it is.

Henry (*nodding, and licking his lips*) Let's suppose, let's just suppose we did have one ...

Sophia What? A chicken!

Martha Henry! Don't you dare!

Sophia You have a chicken?

Henry Now, now, I didn't actually say——

Sophia Listen, everyone: this man from the North, he has a chicken!

There is a huge cheer from the Villagers

Martha Henry, I hope you know what you're doing!

Henry Darling, I understand these people. Diplomacy, clear, concise thinking, that's what we need. All right, everyone, quiet please! Quiet! Quiet, now! Thank you. Thank you very much. Good, excellent. Splendid. Now, let's get down to—er—to—er—oh, dear, where, where exactly was I?

Sophia Chicken. Stone soup with chicken.

Henry Ah, yes, yes. Ah, but, er—no, no, no.

Sophia No, no, no?

Henry No, no, no—not chicken. Hypothetical chicken.

Sophia Hypo — what — ical?

Henry Let us suppose, let us just suppose, hypothetically, simply for the purposes of speculation and conjecture, that we did indeed have a chicken ——

Sophia Is this a real chicken? Or a hypothetical chicken?

Henry A real chicken. Hypothetically.

Sophia A real, hypothetical chicken, I see.

Henry You do? Excellent. Well ...?

Sophia Well, what?

Henry Well, supposing we did, supposing we did have one: what would be your position? I mean, could we — could we reach some kind of understanding?

Sophia What? With the chicken?

Henry No, no, no, not the chicken — you and I. Between you and I.

Sophia What kind of understanding?

Henry Well, since Mrs North and I have already been most generous *vis-à-vis* the cooking pot, I think in the circumstances, taking everything into account, and paying proper and due regard to all extenuating economic circumstances, it would be only reasonable for you to procure, or rather acquire, that is to say purchase outright exclusively and entirely all benefits and liabilities pertaining to said chicken.

Sophia You mean you want us to buy it?

Henry Precisely.

Sophia But how? We have no money.

Henry My dear lady, no problem: we simply arrange credit. Eat now, pay later. Simple. Pay us whatever you like ——

Sophia Mr North ——

Henry — any old cash crop'll do ... cotton, tobacco ——

Sophia Mr North ——

Henry — roses. Yes, even roses; there's always a good demand for ——

Sophia Mr North, please understand: either we all eat stone soup with chicken, or none of us does.

Henry I say, that's a bit extreme.

Sophia All or none, that is how it must be.

Henry I don't think I like your tone.

Sophia Then you don't like the truth; deny us, and you deny yourselves. There is no other way.

Henry Yes there is. Suppose we had two pots.

Sophia Two pots?

Henry One for us and one for the — for the others.

Sophia Mr North ——

Henry Equal but different.

Sophia No, Mr North.

Henry Very well, all right, what if we were to ——?

Sophia No! I have said no!

Henry You might at least have the common courtesy ——

Sophia No, no, no! One world, one people, one pot! That is how it must be. And if you don't like it, you can take your chicken and stuff it!

Henry Well, really!

Sophia ignores him, angrily stirring the soup

Villagers Bloop, bloop, bloop, bloop ... Bloop, bloop, bloop, bloop ... Bloop, bloop, bloop, bloop ...

The Thin Girl approaches again

Thin Girl Please ...

Sophia Yes, my dear, what is it? Oh, it's you again.

Thin Girl Please, is it ready yet?

Sophia Haven't I told you a hundred times? Eh? Haven't I? You must be patient and you must wait!

Thin Girl But it's for my brother. He's dying. I don't think he can wait.

Sophia (*kneeling and holding the Thin Girl*) My dear child, forgive me; I've done all I can, there is nothing more I can do. But tell your brother, tell him to hold on to his life, to hold very tight because soon, soon my soup it will be ready, and I promise, I promise, he will be the first.

Thin Girl (*sadly turning away*) Thank you.

Martha sniffs. Henry comforts her, dabbing her eyes

Henry Didn't I tell you? Didn't I say we shouldn't come? All this suffering. You know how it upsets you.

Martha Henry ...

Henry Yes, darling?

Martha Go get the chicken.

The Villagers give a huge cheer. Henry hugs Martha

THINK OF THE MAGIC
by Frank Rodgers

With the help of an old magic kettle and a genie, the Carr family, with a group of children known as the Phantoms, have entered the 'pantomime' world. The kettle has been snatched by the evil ones and without it, the Genie cannot return the Carrs and the Phantoms to the real world and home. In these two scenes, King Beef's palace and the Sorceror's cave, Dame Pye, a relative of the King's, has arrived with 'the motley crew' in search of help to find the evil one's cave and the kettle.

Set: King Beef's palace; the Sorceror's cave.

Cast: M8 F9. Extras.
Miss Hatchett, King Beef's secretary, stern exterior hiding a passionate heart. Captain Bullseye, pantomime-idiot type, nervous. King Beef, 'his red nose and cheeks and an ample girth seem to point to a personage of some jollity', now down in the dumps. Herald. Princess Alice, fairytale/pantomime model. Dame Pye, pantomime dame, formidable, brash, kind-hearted. Jimmy Carr, image-conscious big brother; 16. Jackie and Maggie Carr, twins. Tracey Carr, starry-eyed; 18. Dinky Carr, tomboy tearaway, leader of the Phantom gang; 10. Ronetta Carr, weird one of the family. Billy and Simmy, two Phantom gang members. The Royal Burghers at the King's palace. Slygrimm, evil sorcerer, tall but ineffectual. Horrenda, his wife, a small but very nasty sorceress. Monster, their eldest son, typical pantomime dope, looks scary but lovable with it. The Brood, the sorcerers' other children.

Playing time: 20 minutes.

SCENE A

King Beef's palace

A flat or curtain shows the crest of the Royal House of Beef with motto, "Done to a turn" and designs or motifs of beef, sausages, pies etc. incorporated in the set

Miss Hatchet, King Beef's secretary, enters

Miss Hatchet Oh, it's not easy being King Beef's secretary. What a job I have just to keep him organized! He's so slow, and does he listen to me half the time? No, he does not. "Don't bother with this, don't bother with that, Miss Hatchet. It'll take care of itself." But of course it never does. I'm the one who has to take care of everything, from his socks to his shopping. What an eater! Always on about food. So I've put him on a diet—but it's just made him depressed! The way I take care of him I may as well be his wife. (*She falters and blushes*) Oh, what have I said? King Beef's wife? But you know, it's true! I *would* like to be his wife. I'm not ashamed of it. Oh, King Beef! Oh, Beefy! How I'd love to tell you of my secret passion. How I want to put my arms around you, my own little—beef sandwich! If only there was a way!

Sound of a fanfare. She comes back to reality and her stern exterior

Oh, that means he'll be here at any moment. I'd better get the Royal Burgers in here to form a guard of honour. Captain Bullseye!

Captain Bullseye enters. He is nervous and obviously in awe of Miss Hatchet

Captain Bullseye Er—yes—Miss Hatchet?
Miss Hatchet Get King Beef's Burgers in here at once, Captain.
Captain Bullseye Certainly, Miss Scratchit—I mean Matchstick—I mean Heartsick ...

Miss Hatchet moves forward threateningly

(*Backing away*) Oh, dear ... I say, men! In here at the double. Er—quick march and all that!

The Royal Burgers enter. They do not inspire confidence

One two, one—two—er—left, right—er right—left—er left.

The Burgers are now about as organized as the Keystone Cops—falling over each other, etc.

Miss Hatchet (*looking on in disbelief*) Halt!

The Burgers come to a ragged halt

Captain Bullseye (*put out by the interference*) I say, Miss Backstitch ... er Snitchback ... er Hatchet, dash it all! This is my troop!
Miss Hatchet You are a nincompoop, Captain. What are you?
Captain Bullseye Oh, I say, Miss F-F-Flatskip—that's a bit strong ...

Miss Hatchet What are you?
Captain Bullseye A nincompoop, Miss Hatchback. Thank you, Miss Handshake.
Miss Hatchet (*wearily*) Get in line, Captain.
Captain Bullseye Right away, Miss—er—right away. (*He stands in line*)

Sound of a fanfare

The Herald enters

Herald My Lords, Ladies and Gentlemen! Pray stand to attention for your Royal Game Monarch, His Meatiness ... King Beef!

King Beef enters. His red nose and cheeks and an ample girth seem to point to a personage of some jollity. But King Beef is down in the dumps due to an enforced low-calorie diet

King Beef Miss Hatchet ...
Miss Hatchet Your wish is my command, your Prime Cutness.
King Beef It's one of those days, Miss Hatchet. My cousin, Ruby, Dame Pye, has arrived with a motley crew of people. She's in a real *stew*, got this *cooked-up, half-baked* story about a magic lamp. Oh, this conversation is making me hungry. Couldn't I just have a teensy T-bone steak with creamed potatoes, onion rings, doughballs, fried bread, buttered carrots, gravy and a side salad?
Miss Hatchet Of course, your Pieness.
King Beef What?
Miss Hatchet Well, what I mean is, you can have the side salad.
King Beef (*studying his ample girth*) Oh, groan! I'm fading away!
Miss Hatchet You said something about a magic lamp, your Meatiness?
King Beef Yes, silly, isn't it? It's supposed to be able to do anything.
Miss Hatchet Anything!? (*Excited, aside*) Perhaps it would give me a wish and I could win his love! Oh!
King Beef But those two bad *eggs* Slygrimm and Horrenda have stolen it. It's all too much. As my Italian chef used to say, "It's a *pizza* nonsense and *pasta* joke!" Oh, I'm hungry again! Miss Hatchet, your monarch is melancholy, your ruler is restless, your chief is *cheesed* off! Oh, there I go again! I'm glad you've got entertainment organized for tonight. It'll take my mind off food!
Miss Hatchet I'm afraid the entertainment's been cancelled, your Meatiness.
King Beef Cancelled? Oh no! I was looking forward to it. What happened?
Miss Hatchet It was my fault. I got the—dates—mixed up.
King Beef *Dates?* (*Weakly*) Oh, I'm disappointed in you, Miss Hatchet.
Miss Hatchet But, your Pieness——
King Beef Don't interrupt me when I'm being miserable.
Miss Hatchet But——
King Beef Oh, go away, Miss Hatchet.

Miss Hatchet You—Your Majesty?

King Beef Leave me alone.

Miss Hatchet Leave you?

King Beef Yes ... go away. You're dismissed! Take a holiday! (*He turns away and slumps on his throne, depressed*)

Miss Hatchet (*stunned, then furious*) Why, after all I've done for him. After giving him the best years of my life. He treats me like that! (*She looks at King Beef*) The ungrateful b-barrel of lard! Oh, I'll make him sorry! I'll make him pay! But how? I know! The magic lamp! He said it could do anything. That's it! Just the thing to help me. I'll find out about it from those children, then—I'll find the sorcerers!

Miss Hatchet exits

Princess Alice enters, a fairytale/pantomime model

Princess Alice Really, Father—I heard you as I came in. I'm ashamed of you, talking to Miss Hatchet like that!

King Beef I'm sorry, Alice, but it's your Aunt Ruby. She gets on my nerves. She treats me like a baby!

Princess Alice Oh, I'm sure she doesn't.

Dame Pye (*off*) Beefykins!

King Beef Oh, no! What did I tell you? (*He gets up and starts to back away*)

Dame Pye enters in full sail

Dame Pye Ah, Beefykins, there you are you naughty boy! Now you must listen, I've got to talk to you!

Dame Pye propels King Beef off stage

Princess Alice (*laughing*) Poor Dad!

Jimmy enters. He approaches Princess Alice with studied casualness

Jimmy This is a strange place, Princess Alice ...

Princess Alice (*looking round*) Is it? I'm used to it.

Jimmy No, I meant this kingdom and ... er ... you ... being here.

Princess Alice Me?

Jimmy Yeh—well what I mean is, I know you were here anyway, but you're so like my—er ... and Vince back there—he's so like ... It's like—er ... (*He is lost for words*) Weird!

Maggie and Jackie enter

Princess Alice I see, I think.

Jackie See our big brother—he's really articulate.
Maggie No wonder. The only thing he ever reads are the backs of Cornflake packets.

Dinky and the Phantoms enter exuberantly

Billy This is some place!

The children crowd round the Burgers

Dinky Real swords! Real sorcerers! This is magic!
Simmy (*to the captain*) Can I have a shot of your helmet, General?
Captain Bullseye General, eh? I say, what fun—why not?
Dinky (*to a Burger*) Can I try on your cloak?
Burger Certainly squire!

*The other children and Burgers join in. The children dress up in the over-size items
and a knockabout routine follows*

Tracey, Vince, Genie, Sandra and Ronnetta enter

Tracey Dinky! Billy! Stop this! Behave yourselves!

King Beef enters, followed by Dame Pye

King Beef What's the meaning of this? (*He surveys his Burgers who are in various
states of undress and still clowning around*) Get up! Where's your dignity? Call
yourselves Beefburgers?
Dinky But, Tracey ...
Tracey Give them back!

The Phantoms give the items back

Ronnetta And I'll have my gloves.

Dinky hands them back

King Beef (*slumping on his throne*) Oh, today's been too much!
Dame Pye Poor Beefykins!
King Beef I'm a depressed despot.
Dame Pye (*patting his corporation*) Well you could certainly do with a bit of
depressing here, dear.

King Beef gives her a look

Please yourself.

Genie Your Meatiness, we need to know the whereabouts of the sorcerer's cave.

King Beef That's a mystery. Not even the Royal VAT man knows where that is! Oh, I'm a limp lord. A listless liege!

Ronnetta Hey, be cool, King. Hang loose.

King Beef If I thought it would cheer me up, I'd hang anybody.

Ronnetta What you need is a shot of Rhythm and Blues from Doctor Dance and Mister Beat!

Jackie Great idea! (*She realizes she doesn't know what Ronnetta is talking about*) What?

Ronnetta You know what I mean, Jackie. A little bit of electric boogie will cheer up our noble nibs here, no bother!

Princess Alice Electric boogie, Ronnetta? You're talking about body-poppin', flip-flop, breakdance—even good old Rock 'n' Roll?

Ronnetta Hey, Alice, you speak my language.

Sandra I'm glad somebody does.

Princess Alice Oh, Ronnetta. I'm so glad you came. Father's so stuffy—and I just love Rock 'n' Roll.

King Beef (*groaning*) Loves Rock 'n' Roll! My daughter! The shame of it!

Ronnetta (*to Alice*) Don't worry, he'll come round once his toe starts tapping. Shall we? (*She poses*)

To the amazement of all, Princess Alice does a quick change to reveal a Rock 'n' Roll costume underneath her gown. It could simply require the skirt to be slipped off to reveal brightly coloured tights, legwarmers, etc.

Princess Alice Let's go, Ronnetta!

An optional rock 'n' roll dance sequence follows. During the song, King Beef stays slumped in this throne ... until he is persuaded, at the appropriate point, to join the others ... where he demonstrates a remarkable grasp of jiving

All DIG THAT CRAZY MONARCH!

Ronnetta (*speaking in a rapping beat*)
　　　　Well come on ev'rybody take a look at your king
　　　　Beating out a royal rhythm, doin' his regal thing!
　　　　He's got diamonds in his crown but let me tell you the news,
　　　　He's got diamond-studded laces in his blue-suede shoes!
　　　　Well gimme a K!

All (*shouting*) K!

Ronnetta Gimme an I!

All I!

Ronnetta Gimme an N!

All N!

Ronnetta Gimme a G!
All G!
Ronnetta Put together with Beef, you got rockin' royalty.

Black-out

SCENE B

The sorcerer's cave

Effective use can be made of simple cut-out shapes (rocks, bats, spiders, etc.)

Horrenda is poring over a large volume whilst Slygrimm stands at her side with the lamp, Monster practises making faces in a mirror and the Brood annoy each other in the background

Horrenda Quiet, you brats!

Everyone falls silent

(*Turning back to the book*) Nearly at the end—it must be here! (*She reads*)

Slygrimm rubs the kettle

   Zemi?
Slygrimm No.
Horrenda Zeppelin?
Slygrimm No.
Horrenda Zodiac?
Slygrimm No.
Monster Zombie?
Slygrimm No.
Horrenda Zootomy?
Slygrimm NO.
Horrenda Zoroastrianism?
Slygrimm No.
Horrenda The last one. It has to be—Zymotic!?
Slygrimm No.
Horrenda Rats! We've gone through the whole of the *Witch Report* and still haven't found the magic word!
Monster Let me beat it out of it, eh, Mum?
Slygrimm Horrenda, dearest ...
Horrenda (*eagerly*) Yes, you have an idea?

Slygrimm No, it's just that my hand's sore rubbing this lamp.
Horrenda Fool!

Miss Hatchet enters

*The Brood hiss quietly as Miss Hatchet walks boldly up to Slygrimm who has his
back to her. She taps him on the shoulder, giving him the fright of his life*

(*Venomously*) You are Hatchet! From the palace!
Miss Hatchet I am. I take it you are the—(*disdainfully*)—sorcerers?
Slygrimm I am he ...
Horrenda (*pushing him aside*) And what if we are? (*She motions to the Brood*)

The Brood begin to circle Miss Hatchet, making weird noises and chanting

Brood   Hatchet's going to catch it! Hatchet's going to catch it!
                    Hatchet's going to catch it! Hatchet's going to——
Miss Hatchet That's quite enough!

The Brood hesitate, unsure

Stop this ridiculous behaviour immediately!

They stop

Now, pay attention when I'm talking to you.

They do, and to Horrenda's annoyance so do Slygrimm and Monster

Stand up, straight!

They do so

Arms folded!

They do so

Sit!

They do so, mouths agape

Mouths shut!

The Brood do so. Miss Hatchet turns to Slygrimm and Monster who are still standing

with their mouths open. Slygrimm and Monster look at her and shut their mouths.
Miss Hatchet turns to the audience by way of explanation

I used to be a primary teacher.
Slygrimm What do you want with us?
Miss Hatchet I have come to strike a bargain with you, distasteful as I find it.
Monster Let me rough her up a little, Mum!
Horrenda (*restraining him*) Not now, darling. (*To Miss Hatchet*) What kind of bargain could you possibly——
Miss Hatchet Concerning the magic lamp.
Sorcerers The lamp?
Miss Hatchet Yes, the lamp. *You* have it—*I* can get you someone who knows the magic word. On one condition.
Horrenda (*suspiciously*) What's the condition?
Miss Hatchet That I have three wishes. I have a score to settle.
Horrenda We'll think about it.
Slygrimm We will?

Horrenda gives him a look

We will! Of course we will!

Slygrimm, Horrenda and Monster move aside. Miss Hatchet inspects the Brood

What shall we do with her?
Horrenda Nothing.
Slygrimm Nothing?
Horrenda Yet! We'll agree to her condition, then, when we have the magic word— (*she grins meaningfully*)—we'll dispose of her!
Slygrimm That's absolutely dishonest, wicked, dirty-dealing, two-faced and treacherous!
Horrenda I know, lovely, isn't it?
Slygrimm (*rubbing his hands in glee*) Wonderful!
Monster I just love my mum. She's so TWISTED!

The sorcerers join Miss Hatchet

Horrenda We accept your bargain. Bring us someone who knows the magic word and you shall have your three wishes.
Miss Hatchet Very well. (*She turns to go*)
Horrenda (*stopping her*) But the children go with you so that there's no funny business! The young darlings are at a very impressionable age, so mind your language. No eight-letter words!
Miss Hatchet Eight-letter words? Goodness!

All That's the one!

During the following the evil ones gather round Miss Hatchet who is beginning to look less sure of herself

Slygrimm
Horrenda } (*together*) We are evil and we like it.
Monster

Brood   Ooh yes we like it.

Slygrimm
Horrenda } (*together*) Guard your drink or else we'll spike it.
Monster

Brood   Ooh yes we'll spike it.

Slygrimm
Horrenda } (*together*) We are bad from top to bottom.
Monster

Brood   Need we say more?

Slygrimm
Horrenda } (*together*) We are absolutely rotten.
Monster

Brood   Rotten to the core.

Slygrimm
Horrenda } (*together*) We are sickeningly, absolutely vile,
Monster

All   And we never never never ever smile!

Slygrimm
Horrenda } (*together*) We are nasty and we know it.
Monster

Brood   Ooh yes we know it.

Slygrimm
Horrenda } (*together*) Watch your mind or else we'll blow it.
Monster

Brood   Ooh yes we'll blow it.

Slygrimm
Horrenda } (*together*) We invented smelly cheeses.
Monster

Brood   Like Camembert and Gruyère.

Slygrimm
Horrenda } (*together*) We concocted new diseases.
Monster

Brood   We're rotten through and through, yeh.

Slygrimm
Horrenda } (*together*) But we're running out of horrible things to do.
Monster

All	So now we're going to concentrate on you!
	But whatever you do, don't mention the word GOODNESS,
Miss Hatchet	Goodness?
All	YEUK! That's the word that makes us want to be sick!
	Whenever we feel some goodness coming on,
	We send for the witch doctor quick!

The sorcerers and the Brood close round Miss Hatchet

We are EVIL! BAD! DESPICABLE! ROTTEN! TWO-FACED! UNDERHAND!
NASTY! SHIFTY!
Slygrimm Not very nice.
All AAAHAHAHAHAHAHAHAHA!

They exit with Miss Hatchet who is beginning to look sick about the whole affair

Black-out

THE WATER BABIES
adapted by Willis Hall, from the story by Charles Kingsley

Charles Kingsley's classic, set in mid-Victorian times, tells of Tom's adventures, first as apprentice to Mr Grimes, the bullying chimney-sweep, and then his underwater journey to the Other-End-of-Nowhere. Young Tom wishes only to find Ellie, whom he accidentally met when working, and Mrs Doasyouwouldbedoneby helps him on his final journey. His first task is to visit Mr Grimes in prison. These two scenes could be staged on two levels.

Set:
The Other-End-of-Nowhere opens with only an iron door, then leads into a prison and the chimney where Mr Grimes's head and shoulders only are seen. This scene moves into the final scene: Back On Dry Land, where Ellie's four-poster bed is seen. Period: mid Victorian.

Cast: M7 F4. 4 off-stage voices.
Tom, a chimney-sweep's apprentice, about 11 years old. Thomas Grimes, a chimney-sweep. 1st and 2nd Warders, stern-looking Victorian prison warders. Mrs Bedonebyasyoudid, a formidable lady in black bonnet and black shawl, she wears large green spectacles and a great hooked nose. In the last scene, she transforms into Mrs Doasyouwouldbedoneby and the Irishwoman. Ellie, a girl about 11 with cheeks 'white as the pillow' and 'hair like threads of gold'. Sir John, the Doctor, the Housemaid, the Nurse and the Gamekeeper stand around the bed. 4 voices off-stage.

Playing time: 12 minutes.

SCENE A

The Other-End-of-Nowhere

Where at first and with Tom, all we can see is an iron door. Tom hammers on the door with his fists and the sound echoes off into the gloom. The door squeaks open and Tom finds himself confronted by:

Two stern-looking men with mutton-chop whiskers and dressed in the uniforms of Victorian prison warders

1st Warder Stand up straight and state your business.

Tom If it please you, sir, but could you tell me if this is the Other-End-Of-Nowhere?

2nd Warder What if it is? Do you have to make such a noise about it?

Tom If it is sir, I'd like to come in.

1st Warder Come in? Come in! We never 'as folks as wants to come in 'ere! And them what is in 'ere already is only anxious to get out—not that we ever lets 'em. Name and sentence?

Tom My name is Tom—but I haven't been sentenced to anything, sir—is it a prison then?

2nd Warder Of course it's a prison, laddie—what else might you expect to find at the Other-End-Of-Nowhere, a seaside pier and prom? And if you 'aven't come 'ere to serve a sentence, might one enquire your purpose?

Tom I'm looking for Mr Grimes, the master chimney-sweep.

1st Warder Grimes? 'Im! That blaggard. 'Ee's not entitled to visitors. Why 'ee's the most unremorseful, hard-hearted, foul-mouthed fellow we've got in charge. What makes you think we'd let you see him?

Tom Mrs Doasyouwouldbedoneby sent me.

2nd Warder Then why didn't you say so in the first place—wasting my time. Come in.

Tom goes through the door which closes slowly behind him

1st Voice (*off*) Visitor for Prisoner Grimes!

2nd Voice (*off*) Visitor for Prisoner Grimes!

3rd Voice (*off*) Pass visitor to chimney number three-five-four!

4th Voice (*off*) Chimney number three-five-four!

We shall hear as many or as few voices as are required and they might also be accompanied by the sound of echoing footsteps along stone-flagged passages

Then as the Light gradually grows, we begin to make out through the gloom a chimney which has Grimes's head and shoulders sticking out of it. In silhouette, beyond Grimes, we can make out a vast array of chimneys stretching off into the distance. Tom and the Warders approach him

1st Warder Attention Mr Grimes! Stand to attention there!

Grimes Attention be blowed. 'Ow can a body stand to attention when 'ee's all jammed up a chimbley and can't so much as twiddle the end of 'is little finger!

At which point, the Warder bangs Grimes over the head with his truncheon

Ow! That 'urt!

2nd Warder It was meant to 'urt, prisoner Grimes. 'Ere's a gentleman come to see you.

Grimes Why, Tom! If it ain't Tom!

Tom Hallo, Mr Grimes. How are you keeping?

Grimes 'Ow am I keeping? 'Ow am I keeping, you young ragamuffin? 'Ow does it look as if I'm keeping? 'Ow would you keep jammed up all day and all night in a blessed chimbley and not able to do so much as twiddle the end of your little finger?

The Warder wallops Grimes over the head with his truncheon for a second time

Ow-er! To say nothing of being banged over the 'ead reg'lar as clockwork with a great galloping truncheon! I suppose you've come 'ere to laugh at me, you spiteful little street-arab!

Tom No, Mr Grimes—I came to see if I could help you.

Grimes There's nothing I want, excepting beer, and that I can't get—and to smoke just a pipeful of baccy, perhaps, but that I can't get to neither.

Grimes nods down at his pipe which is sticking up out of his breast pocket. Tom reaches to take it out

Tom I'll put your pipe in your mouth for you, Mr Grimes——

But the Warder takes the pipe from Tom, sticks it back in Grimes's pocket and shakes his head, as:

1st Warder It's no good. You'll never manage to light it. His heart's that cold it freezes everything that comes close to him—can't you feel the chill coming out of him now? (*He shivers involuntarily*) Brrr!

Grimes Oh, of course, it's my fault! Is it any wonder I'm frozen to death—stood standing still in this damp, dark, pestilential prison day after day, week after week, month after month—everything's always *my* fault!

1st Warder And isn't it your fault—or are we to hear more of your excuses? Excuses, excuses, Grimes, always excuses ...

Tom Isn't there anything that I can do to assist you, Mr Grimes? Can't I help you to get out of this chimney?

Grimes shakes his head sadly, as:

2nd Warder Nay, lad. He has come to the place where everybody must help themselves—and the sooner he realizes that, the better.

Grimes Oh yes, of course it's me. Did I ask to be brought here into the prison? Did I ask to be set to sweep your foul chimbleys? Did I ask to have lighted straw put under me to make me clamber up?

And, suddenly, out of the shadows, steps Mrs Bedonebyasyoudid

Mrs Bedonebyasyoudid (*addressing Grimes sternly*) No! No more did Tom, when you behaved to him in the very same way.

Warders (*leaping to attention*) Ma'am!

Tom Oh, ma'am don't think about me, that's all past and gone, and good times and bad times all pass over. But may I not help poor Mr Grimes? Mayn't I try and get some of these bricks away that he may move his arms?

Mrs Bedonebyasyoudid You may try, of course.

Tom tugs and pulls at the brickwork, but to no avail

Tom It's no good, Mr Grimes—I've come all this way to help you, and now I'm no use at all.

Grimes Nay, lad, you'd best leave me be. You're a kindhearted little lad, and that's the truth—but you'd best be off. It'll start to hail again soon, and that'd beat the eyes out of your head.

Tom How do you know it's going to hail?

Grimes Because it allus rains in this hole—as soon as it's night—hard, driving chunks of hail like pellets of lead.

Mrs Bedonebyasyoudid That hail will never come again, Grimes. I have told you before what that was—your mother's tears, those that she shed when she prayed for you while she was alive—but now the poor woman is dead.

Grimes So ... So, my old mother's gone then, has she? She was a good-hearted woman, lad, but I treated her bad—ay, and never sent her back so much as a penny-piece after I left. And now it's too late ... too late! (*He begins to sob, softly at first, but growing in volume*) It's all too late. Go on with thee, thou little man, and don't stand to look at a fellow old enough to be your father that's reduced to tears. I've made my bed and I must lie on it. Foul I would be, and foul I am, as an Irishwoman once told me. It's all too late ...

Mrs Bedonebyasyoudid It's never too late, Grimes—never too late for a man to regret his past and help himself—and your own tears have washed away the mortar that has held you fast.

Grimes (*wriggling excitedly*) She's right, Tom—by God, she's right! I'm coming loose! Now, lad, you *can* give me a helping hand!

Tom begins to lift down sections of brickwork, perhaps assisted by the Warders

Tom It is loose, Mr Grimes, sir—and easy now to shift—it don't even *feel* like bricks any longer—it's like lifting feathers ...

Mrs Bedonebyasyoudid And shall you obey me in future, Grimes, if I give you this second chance?

Grimes Shall I not! You're stronger than me, and wiser too, and that I know too well. And as for being my own master, I've fared ill enough along that path.

Mrs Bedonebyasyoudid Be it so, then, Grimes—and now you may step out.

Grimes gets down out of the chimney

But remember always: disobey me once, and into a worse place still you go.

Grimes Oh, your ladyship, I'll not do that.

Mrs Bedonebyasyoudid (*to the 1st Warder*) Take him away then.

1st Warder And what am I to do with him, ma'am?

Mrs Bedonebyasyoudid He hasn't *quite* finished his punishment yet. Set him to sweeping out the insides of a couple of dead volcanoes—that should keep him occupied for a year or two—and then, when he is done, I shall review his case again.

Grimes (*as he is led away, apparently overjoyed*) Volcanoes, mum? Oh, bless you, mum! It'll be a pleasure, mum! Thank you, mum! Dead volcanoes! God love you, mum!

Grimes and the Warders exit

Mrs Bedonebyasyoudid turns back to Tom

Mrs Bedonebyasyoudid And now your task is done here, Tom—you can go back to where you came from.

Tom That's easier said than done, ma'am—it took me such a time to get here, shall it take as long to get home again?

Mrs Bedonebyasyoudid Bless the child, of course it won't! For I shall send you back the secret way—up the private back-staircase.

Tom And where might that be, ma'am?

Mrs Bedonebyasyoudid Wherever I say it is, of course. Here, take my hand and close your eyes—and then forget as soon as you have heard them, these magic words:

Oh, backstairs; well-bred backstairs; precious backstairs; commercial backstairs; invaluable backstairs; economical backstairs; requisite backstairs; cosmopolitan backstairs; comfortable backstairs; comprehensive backstairs; accommodating backstairs; reasonable backstairs; aristocratic backstairs; demonstrable backstairs; potent backstairs; all-but-omnipotent backstairs—save us from the consequences of our own actions, and from the cruel fairy, Mrs Bedonebyasyoudid!

As she has recited the "magic words", the music has crept in behind and now the lighting changes into several flashing colours, and then dims—leaving Tom and Mrs Bedonebyasyoudid in a spot as we go to:

SCENE B

Back On Dry Land

Where the four-poster bed has again been trucked on but is, for the moment, invisible in the darkness

Mrs Bedonebyasyoudid Now you are safely up the stairs and home again and all is well.

Tom (*opening his eyes*) But what about Ellie, ma'am?
Mrs Bedonebyasyoudid Heaven's sakes, child, when I say that all is well I mean all is well! I don't go in for half-measures!

The lighting grows and now we can see the four-poster with the group consisting of Sir John; the Doctor; the Housemaid; the Nurse and the Gamekeeper standing in frozen attitudes around it. They remain "frozen" as Ellie gets up off the bed and runs across to join Tom. Mrs Bedonebyasyoudid moves back into shadow. Tom and Ellie take hold of each other's hands and gaze into each other's face

Tom Ellie—oh, Ellie! You *are* quite better—you are quite well!
Ellie And Tom—oh, Tom—it *isn't* a dream any longer—you're safe and real! (*Embracing him*) And not prickly and spiky any longer!
Mrs Bedonebyasyoudid Enough of that! Attention, both of you—now look at me, and tell me who I am.
Tom You're Mrs Bedonebyasyoudid.

But as she moves out of the shadows we see that she has turned into Mrs Doasyouwouldbedoneby

Ellie You're Mrs Doasyouwouldbedoneby!

And now she removes her half-mask and we see that she has now become the Irishwoman

Tom Ecky Moses! You're the Irishwoman I met on the day I went to Harthover.
Irishwoman I am all of them and I am none of them, as you will one day learn—but not yet, young things, not yet. You have your lives before you.

Index of authors